KU-670-488

LIFE SCIENCE LIBRARY

LIFE SCIENCE LIBRARY

WATER

by Luna B. Leopold, Kenneth S. Davis
and the Editors of TIME-LIFE BOOKS

CONSULTING EDITORS

René Dubos
Henry Margenau
C. P. Snow

TIME-LIFE INTERNATIONAL (NEDERLAND) N.V.

ABOUT THIS BOOK

THE STORY OF WATER is in many ways the story of life itself. Water is the major substance of every living thing on earth. Man is dependent on it not only for drinking but also for power, transportation and irrigation. As modern technology demands more and more water, ways must be constantly devised to tap new resources and to make re-usable the water man has polluted.

The book tells of the nature of water, what it can do and how it is used by man. Each text chapter is supplemented by a picture essay, which may be read independently. For example, Chapter 2, "A Sun-powered Cycle", explains the hydrologic cycle; it is followed by a picture essay entitled "The Long Voyage from Sea to Sea", which offers a different perspective on the same ceaseless journey that water makes from sea to atmosphere to land, and back to sea.

THE AUTHORS

LUNA B. LEOPOLD, research hydrologist with the U.S. Geological Survey, is also a civil engineer, meteorologist and geologist. He is author of more than 100 scientific papers, and co-author of *The Flood Control Controversy* and *Fluvial Processes in Geomorphology*. Dr. Leopold has received the Kirk Bryan award of the Geological Society of America and the Veth Medal of the Royal Netherlands Geographical Society. He was recently elected to membership of the U.S. National Academy of Sciences.

KENNETH S. DAVIS is author of *River on the Rampage* and co-author of *Water: The Mirror of Science*. Mr. Davis has also written a number of novels, biographies of the late President Eisenhower and Adlai E. Stevenson, and *Experience of War*, the story of the U.S. in World War II.

THE CONSULTING EDITORS

RENÉ DUBOS, a member and professor of The Rockefeller University, is a distinguished microbiologist and experimental pathologist who was awarded the Arches of Science Award in 1966 and the Pulitzer Prize in 1969 for his book *So Human an Animal: How We Are Shaped by Surroundings and Events*. He is also the author of *Mirage of Health* and *Man Adapting* and co-author of *Health and Disease* in this series.

HENRY MARGENAU is Eugene Higgins Emeritus Professor of Physics and Natural Philosophy at Yale, and an authority in spectroscopy and nuclear physics. He wrote *Open Vistas* and *The Nature of Physical Reality*, and is co-author of *The Scientist* in this series.

C. P. SNOW has won an international audience for his novels, including *The New Men*, *The Affair* and *Corridors of Power*, which explore the effects of science on today's society.

Original English language edition published by TIME Inc. In the United States.

CONTENTS

PREFACE

SOME 15 YEARS AGO, the engineer Thomson King epitomized the water problem in the following terms:

"Of all the substances that are necessary to life as we know it on earth, water is by far the most important, the most familiar, and the most wonderful; yet most people know very little about it."

More poetically, Byron reflected on the same theme in his *Don Juan*:

> "Till taught by pain
> Men really know not what good water's worth."

History is replete with the sagas of armies that fought over water, of monarchs and priests who worshipped it and health workers who have blessed it, of civilizations that dwindled after losing or mismanaging it, of people who died because of it.

Water has many curious facets. It is universally present and has remained unchanged in amount and character over millions of years. It is at once the servant and the master of man. Yet the man on the street is aware of it only when it fails or endangers him. Then its dramatic impact falls with full force—too often accompanied by false impressions, conclusions and solutions.

The present volume should serve to clarify and to place in perspective the mysteries of this exciting commodity and the manifold uses to which it may be put for the benefit of mankind. It explores the nature of this extraordinary substance and reviews its place in the atmosphere, on earth and below the earth's surface. It recalls that the earth's profile was in large measure fashioned by water—and that water eternally continues to reshape the land. Common sense and simplicity of concept and statement abound in the exposition of water's impact upon man and civilization—in antiquity as well as today in virtually every developing country and in some already developed. Realistic appraisals of problems and solutions complete a text long desired.

The effort to disclose to man his dependence upon and his benefits from water is welcome. A society increasingly confronted with water decision-making should at least understand the ingredients of the problem. This book should go far to aid in that understanding.

—ABEL WOLMAN

Professor Emeritus of Geography and Environmental Engineering
The Johns Hopkins University

1

A Maverick Compound

WATER IN ITS MOST AWESOME FORM THUNDERS OVER A SECTION OF THE MILE-LONG VICTORIA FALLS IN AFRICA

In its very ordinariness, water is extraordinary. It is everywhere. In the form of oceans, ice fields, lakes and rivers it covers nearly three-quarters of the earth's surface; these bodies together contain more than 324 million cubic miles of water. Beneath the earth, permeating soil and rock, lies some two million cubic miles more in the form of ground-water. In the earth's atmosphere is another 3,100 cubic miles of water, mostly vapour.

This abundance of water was present when the earth was born, and most scientists believe that life was conceived in the planet's primeval oceans. Water continues to support all life—some very simple organisms can exist without air, but none can grow without water. It has given rise to great civilizations, and sometimes it has been responsible for their destruction. Over hundreds of millions of years, it has been one of the most powerful agents in shaping and reshaping the face of the earth. Frozen into creeping glaciers, it chisels the landscape, gouging out vast depressions and lake beds, switching river courses and carrying soil and boulders over tremendous distances. Falling as rain or in flowing rivers, it levels mighty mountains, creates broad valleys and steep canyons, and weathers the hardest rocks. As pounding waves or lapping surf, it gnaws constantly at coastlines, transforming the profiles of islands and continents. It determines the climate, forms the soil in which crops and forests take root and, as steam or hydroelectric power, it drives the machines of modern technology. It is an indispensable ingredient in nearly all manufacturing processes, from the baking of bread to the manufacture of semi-conductors for transistor radios.

As a substance, water is odourless, colourless and tasteless. Yet it plays an unusual role in the affairs of the world because the seeming insipidity of its properties is deceiving. As a chemical it is unique. It is a compound of great stability, a remarkable solvent and a powerful source of chemical energy. It draws away from most organic substances but is strongly attracted by most inorganic materials, including itself; in fact, its own molecules cling together more tenaciously than those of certain metals. When frozen into a solid it expands, instead of contracting as nearly all other substances do, and the lighter solid floats on the heavier liquid—with astonishing consequences. It can absorb and release more heat than most common substances. In many physical and chemical properties—such as its freezing and boiling temperatures—water is an oddity, an exception to the rules. And nearly every one of these exceptions is woven into the fabric of human life, either naturally, as in the process of digestion, or artificially, as in the steam-engine.

All of water's oddities can be traced to its molecular structure. The combination of two atoms of hydrogen and one of oxygen that comprises water (H_2O) forms a surprisingly sturdy molecule. Tremendous energy is needed to break water apart. In fact, until some 180 years ago water was believed to be an indivisible element rather than a chemical compound.

The converse of water's stability is even more intriguing. For the same reason that hydrogen and oxygen atoms resist being pulled apart, they willingly join together. Any little nudge—striking a match, for instance

—will mate them. The water that "steams" kitchen windows is synthesized in the flames of the stove as hydrogen atoms from the cooking gas unite with oxygen from the air. Even the human body synthesizes water —about 1¾ quarts a week—in the process of metabolizing its food.

Although an exhorbitant amount of energy must be absorbed for the dissociation of water, the same amount is released during its formation. About 1·1 pounds of pure hydrogen and 8·9 pounds of pure oxygen, for example, when combined to produce 10 pounds of water, provide enough energy to keep a 60-watt bulb burning for 325 hours. The hydrogen-oxygen reaction is such a good source of energy that it was put to practical use in the fuel cell that first served as a long-term power generator aboard the Gemini V space craft.

The tie that binds the atoms

This prodigious energy comes entirely from the powerful force which binds two hydrogen atoms to one oxygen atom in the water molecule. The connection is established between the electrons that make up the outer parts of the atoms, and is a strong link called a covalent bond.

The hydrogen atom has a single "shell" around its nucleus and although this shell contains a single electron, it has room for two. The outer shell of the oxygen atom, with room for eight electrons, contains but six. These unfilled shells are not stable—their energetic electrons are precariously held and quick to join with others to fill all the room in a shell. The filled shell is the stable form; once it is created it firmly resists being torn apart.

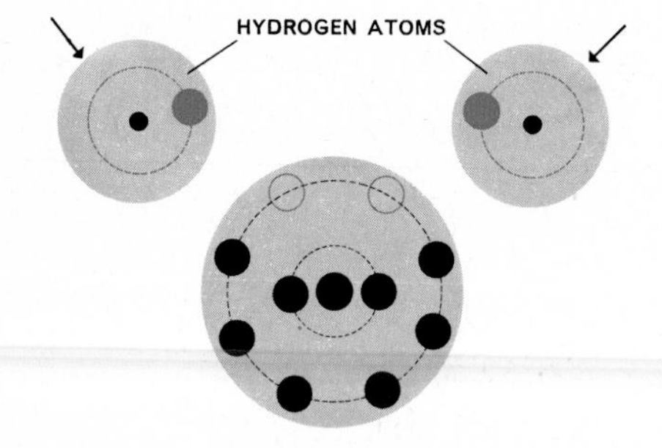

FORMING A WATER MOLECULE, two atoms of hydrogen and an oxygen atom fill their electron orbits by sharing electrons. Each hydrogen atom, with one electron spinning around its nucleus, needs one more electron to become stable. The larger oxygen atom, with six electrons in its outer shell, needs two more to fill its orbit. When the three unstable atoms pool their electrons (*below*), the result is a stable molecule of water.

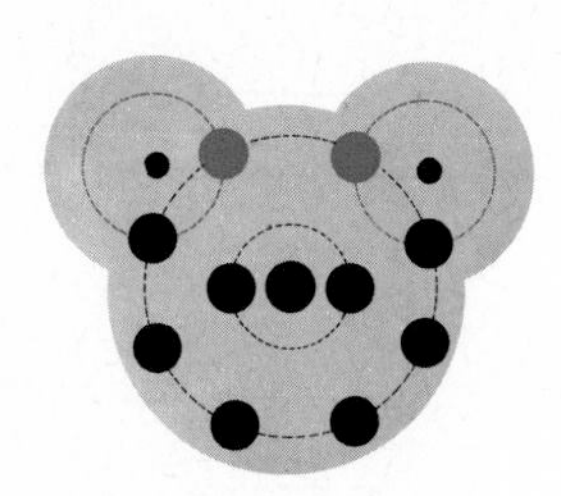

The oxygen atom can fill its shell by adding the electrons from two hydrogen atoms. At the same time, two electrons from the oxygen atom join the shells of the two hydrogen atoms, filling them. That is, the three atoms share their electrons, endowing the water molecule with its remarkable stability.

The covalent bond is the basis for other characteristics of water—its prowess as a solvent, for instance. This quality arises from the shape of the molecule. When two hydrogen atoms link with an oxygen atom, the connection produces a lopsided molecule, with the hydrogen atoms held on one side of the oxygen atom and at an angle of 105° to one another—somewhat like the ears on a rabbit's head. One effect of this mis-shapen structure is an unequal distribution of electric charges. The hydrogen "side" of the water molecule becomes positively charged, while the oxygen side becomes negatively charged. Thus the molecule becomes a dipole—the electrical equivalent of a bar magnet. One side is charged differently from the other, just as a magnet has different poles at each end.

A dipole reacts to electrical charges much as a bar magnet does to magnetism. Its positive side will be attracted to negative charges, its negative side to positive charges. And the electrical force resulting from these charges will counterbalance the influence of other charges. This effect becomes noticeable when water touches certain kinds of compounds.

In many substances, the atoms are held together not by covalent bonds but by a simple electrical attraction. Table salt—sodium chloride—is an example. In this compound, each atom carries opposite electrical charges and therefore attracts the other, to hold the salt molecule together. The molecule will break apart if this attraction between charged atoms, or ions, is blocked.

If a water molecule begins to wedge its way between the two ions that form salt, its dipole effect will cancel some of the electrical attraction between the ions. The weaker attraction permits the ions to move apart, making more room for water and its disruptive dipole effect. In this way water works its way between such ions, cancels their mutual attraction and separates them. The separated ions are then totally surrounded by water—dissolved. Many compounds that are held together by this simple electrical bond, called an ionic bond, readily dissolve in water.

Of all the substances naturally occurring on the face of the earth, water comes closest to being the universal solvent. It is, in fact, such a good solvent that perfectly pure water is very rare, if indeed it occurs at all in nature. The water sipped from a glass may contain, among other things, an infinitesimal number of glass molecules. The very rain, as it condenses and descends, dissolves materials such as atmospheric gases. Wherever it lands, it dissolves still other substances. About half of all the chemical elements are dissolved in natural waters—some of them only as traces, some of them in abundance; every trickle, puddle, lake or sea on earth is an aqueous solution. Sea water is quite a concentrated one; hundreds of organic and inorganic substances, of metals and non-metals, make up the sum total of its "salt".

A non-conforming substance

The lopsidedness which endows the water molecule with such potency as a solvent is also indirectly the source of other exceptional properties. The most significant of these is often overlooked because it is so simple: ice floats. By all the rules of physical behaviour it should not. Almost every substance, whether solid, liquid or gas, will shrink in volume as its temperature goes down. As it contracts, it grows more dense. Thus in its liquid form it is heavier than as a gas, and its solid form is heavier than its liquid.

Water follows this rule precisely as a gas and, as a liquid, for 96 per cent of the way down the temperature range to its freezing point, shrinking steadily all the way. But at 4° C. something happens. As cooling continues the water expands and gets lighter, and as it freezes into a solid at 0° C. it becomes still lighter, until it has finally gained about 9 per cent in volume.

However inconvenient this expansion of ice may be for the householder faced with burst water pipes after a sudden winter freeze, it is fortunate for the rest of the world.

If water behaved like other freezing liquids, there would soon be no life on the earth, for the water would be irrevocably locked in eternal ice on the beds of seas, lakes and streams. As it is, when winter comes, ice forms and floats on the surface of bodies of water, forming an insulating skin which protects the water beneath from further freezing. If ice were heavier than water, it would sink to the bottom and gradually build up from there. Before long the lakes and Arctic seas which now are only superficially covered with ice would be frozen solid, with perhaps thin layers of liquid water over the ice where it melted during the warmest seasons. Most of the world's water supply would become unusable to plants, animals or man.

One of the most spectacular effects to follow such a circumstance would be enormous changes in the world's climate. In this ice-bound world the daily fluctuations of temperature would amount to hundreds of degrees, seasonal variations would be even more radical, and the winds that blow around the world would be parched and searing. For the climate of the world is tempered by the ability of water to soak up and store the sun's heat and to release it slowly.

Heat in freezing water

In the last half of the 18th century a Scottish chemist, Joseph Black, observed with precision part of this mechanism. As recounted by the editor of Black's posthumous *Lectures on the Elements of Chemistry*:

"Since a fine winter day of sunshine did not at once clear the hills of snow, nor a frosty night suddenly cover the ponds with a thick cake of ice, Dr. Black was already convinced that much heat was absorbed and fixed in the water which slowly trickled from the wreaths of snow; and on the other hand, that much heat emerged from it while it was as slowly changing into ice. For, during a thaw, a thermometer will always sink when removed from the air into melting snow; and during severe frost it will rise when plunged into freezing water. Therefore, in the first case, the snow is receiving heat, and in the last, the water is allowing it to emerge again."

From observations such as this, Black discovered two important properties of water. First, he recognized its very large heat capacity, its ability to absorb heat. Heat capacity is expressed in terms of the amount of heat required to raise a given quantity of a substance by a given number of degrees. An enormous amount of heat is needed to warm water—a fact obvious to every housewife who has burned her hand on the pot handle while the water inside the pot was still cool. The iron of a pot will heat up nearly 10 times as fast as water; it requires that much less heat to raise its temperature a given number of degrees.

The second of Black's discoveries was the strange fact of so-called latent heat. It is called latent because it produces no change in temperature; the heat goes entirely into changing the form of a substance. When a solid melts, for example, it absorbs a certain amount of heat—the exact amount depending on the substance—without any increase in temperature until it is entirely melted. If the process is then reversed, the opposite reaction takes place: as the liquid substance freezes it gives up heat without any *lowering* of temperature, the amount given up being exactly equal to the heat it previously had absorbed without a *raising* of temperature.

Water's latent heat is unusually high. To convert ice completely into water—with no change in temperature—requires as much heat as would be needed to bring to the boiling point the same amount of tepid water. This is far more heat than most other common substances require for melting. Iron, for example, melts at 1,517° C.; once the solid is at this temperature, the addition of enough heat to melt a pound of water will melt eight times as much iron. When water again is frozen into ice, it will in the process give up the same heat it absorbed in melting, and this released heat can keep the surroundings warm.

Because of water's latent heat capacity, a tubful of water placed in a greenhouse on a night of freezing cold will act as a reserve supply of heat. Some of its water will be frozen by morning, but the heat it releases during freezing keeps the air inside warmer than the air outside. People living on the seashore experience milder winter temperatures than those who live inland, though both may be swept by the same storms. On the other hand, ice melting in an old-fashioned refrigerator draws heat out of the surrounding food. Similarly, ice cubes chill a drink not so much because the ice is cold but because it melts, absorbing heat from the surrounding fluid in the process.

When a substance evaporates or condenses it gains or loses energy just as it does when melting or freezing. Raise the liquid's temperature to the boiling point and there will be a pause during which heat is absorbed, without a rise in temperature, solely to transform the liquid into gas. If the gas is later steadily cooled, there will also be a pause in temperature decline at the boiling point, though heat will continue to be given off. This pause will endure, and the temperature will remain the same, until all the gas has been liquefied.

The latent heat of evaporation, or its reverse, the latent heat of condensation, is greater for water than it is for most other substances. It takes more than five times as much heat to change boiling-hot water into steam as it does to bring freezing water to a boil. And condensing steam releases exactly the same amount of heat in returning to the liquid state.

Energy from the skies

As a result of water's latent heat, each molecule of water vapour in the atmosphere and each droplet of moisture in a cloud is an airborne bundle of heat energy. It is the dynamic flow of water vapour in our atmosphere that creates global climates and local weather.

The energy locked in water vapour can be observed in the building-up of puffy cumulus clouds into towering thunderheads on a summer day. As the water vapour in the clouds cools and condenses, huge amounts of heat energy are released and the atmosphere inside the clouds boils over with stormy convection currents. The updraughts and downdraughts inside a thunderhead reach hurricane force; the total amount of energy released by a summer thunderstorm is equal to that of a large atomic bomb and

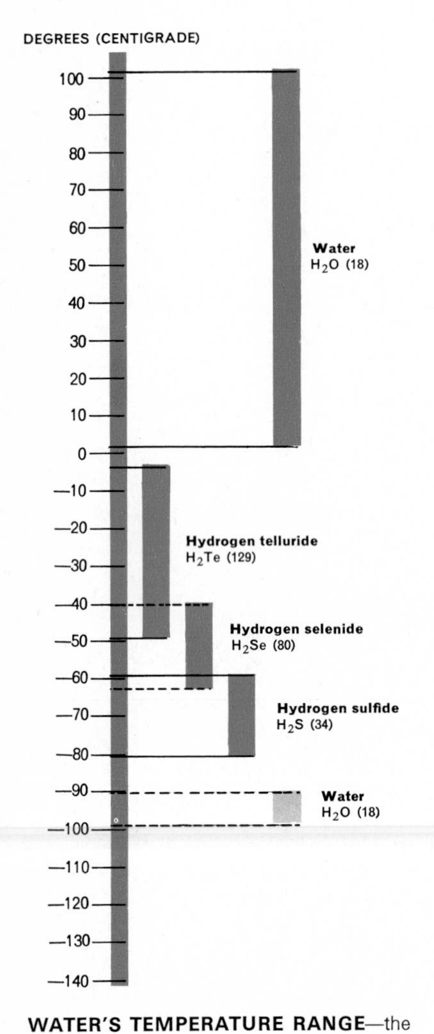

WATER'S TEMPERATURE RANGE—the span between its freezing and boiling points—is curiously out of step with chemical theory, as illustrated by this chart. Substances similar to water (H_2O) in structure—H_2Te, H_2Se, H_2S—descend the scale in a regular pattern: the lower the molecular weight, the lower and narrower the temperature range. Water, with the lowest of the four molecular weights, belongs at the bottom (*pale blue bar*). Instead, it is highest of all. Chemists believe that the strong bonds between the water molecules themselves make it freeze sooner but boil at a higher point than would otherwise be normal.

could cause the same destruction if its energy could be concentrated as it is in a bomb.

Even the temperatures at which water freezes and boils are out of the ordinary. Water freezes at 0° C. and boils at 100° C. This does not fit the pattern set by similar compounds. Most related substances boil and freeze at predictable temperatures: an orderly progression of boiling and freezing points which increase as molecular weight increases. In a group of four compounds chemically related to water, water is the lightest and should have the lowest boiling and freezing points; if water followed the pattern of its chemical sisters it would boil at about —91° C. and freeze at about —100° C.—there could be no liquid water, but only steam at temperatures found on earth. Happily for life on this planet, water is the maverick in the group; its boiling and freezing points are not the lowest but the highest.

The strange relationship between water and heat can be traced to details of water's molecular structure. The lopsided molecule, with electrical charges concentrated on opposite sides, is attracted to other molecules with similar distributions of charges. Negative to positive, these polar molecules link together like so many submicroscopic magnets. This electrical tie, called a hydrogen bond, most readily connects one water molecule to another—the positively charged hydrogen side of one molecule hitches to the negatively charged oxygen side of a near neighbour.

The ice crystal's airy pattern

Since each molecule has two hydrogen positive "terminals" but only one oxygen negative "terminal", the connections build characteristic patterns, such as the six-pointed structures that are familiar in snowflakes. A snowflake's six-pointed star is one modification of a more common form taken by ice crystals. This form is created as each water molecule bonds with four other water molecules, which in turn bond with still others. Thus a system of connections is set up that results in a solid crystal shaped like an elongated pyramid. The inside of the pyramid contains no atoms—it is empty space. As a result it is an airy, lightweight structure. That is why solid water—ice—is lighter than liquid water. In solidifying it shapes itself on to an open skeleton established by hydrogen bonds and held rigid by those bonds.

Only in its solid form are all molecules of water linked together by hydrogen bonds. And the pattern they establish in the solid crystal makes ice float. It accounts for the expansion of water frozen into ice and the odd expansion of liquid water between 0° C. and 4° C.

When ice is heated to melting point, some of the hydrogen bonds break and the patterned arrangement of molecules begins to collapse. When this happens the molecules can move more closely together: the liquid water is denser than the ice from which it was formed. This increase in density, caused by the packing of molecules, continues from the melting point of ice, 0° C. to about 4° C. Within this small temperature range some molecules are still bound together in the ice pattern while others, their hydrogen bonds broken, are free to move around with increasing speed as the temperature is raised. At 4° C. more hydrogen bonds are broken, and enough molecules can speed up to cause water to expand (become less dense) with increasing temperature, the way other substances do.

The tenacious hydrogen bonds—the strongest type of bonds between molecules—are also responsible for the other useful oddities of water's behaviour. Their strength is indicated by the large amounts of energy —heat—that are required to break them. That is why so much heat must be supplied to raise the temperature of water, and why its freezing and boiling points are so abnormally high.

But perhaps the strangest result of the hydrogen bond is water's unusual ability to climb inside tubes, in seeming defiance of gravity. Everyone has observed how the edge of the water in a drinking glass curves slightly upwards, forming a distinct lip-like rim as it clings to and climbs up the sides of the glass. This tendency of liquids to rise along the surface of a solid material is called capillarity. In a very fine tube capillary action is sufficient to lift a column of water against the force of gravity, sometimes to considerable heights, and it is important to the movement of water through soil, the feeding of plants from their roots, and the circulation of the blood.

The tube literally pulls the water up by forming hydrogen bonds between oxygen or nitrogen atoms in the tube material and molecules of water. This attraction raises the water edge. But simultaneously bonds within the water itself are pulling the water surface taut, trying to keep it flat. These opposing actions work in sequence to lift the water inside the tube by a sort of hand-over-hand process. First the water edge rises, then the tension in the water tries to level the surface, and that brings more water near the edge to be lifted higher. The sequence ends only when so much water has been raised that its weight pulling downwards balances the capillary force pulling upwards on the water edge.

Tension at the rim of a water tap

The powerful tension that hydrogen bonds create on a water surface can be seen most clearly at a dripping tap. The horizontal film of water that first appears at the tap's opening acts as if it were a circular piece of very thin transparent rubber. Like an elastic membrane, it slowly bulges as the weight of water it encloses grows greater. But it does not break. Instead, it seems at last to tear itself away from the rim of the tap and to snap around a freely falling drop which, if it were not distorted by air pressure, would be a perfect sphere. Of all possible shapes the sphere is the one having the smallest surface per unit volume. It is the shape in which the falling drop can most tightly, closely pull itself together.

There, in the homely shape of a falling drop, are demonstrated the molecular forces that give water its peculiar properties—those rare qualities that make it the one substance most important to the affairs of this planet.

The Unpredictable Water Molecule

If water, the most common substance on earth, suddenly began to behave as its molecular make-up suggests, life would be overwhelmed by a series of unparalleled disasters. Blood would boil in the body, plants and trees would wither and die, and the world would be transformed into an arid waste. But water molecules are bound together in ways unlike those of any other compound; for this reason they possess properties that are unique and paradoxical.

For example, water is one of the very few substances that are heavier as liquids than as solids. As a liquid, it can creep uphill despite the force of gravity. Water is so benign that immensely diversified forms of life can thrive within it—and so corrosive that, given sufficient time, it will disintegrate the toughest metal. Although it seems to change its form with miraculous ease—sometimes existing simultaneously as a solid, a liquid and a gas around the same river or lake—water actually must yield or absorb prodigious amounts of energy to produce these transformations. In fact, the energy it would take to melt even a small iceberg could drive a large ship across the Atlantic 100 times.

WATER IN THREE FORMS
Water appears in all three of its physical states as a hot stream of liquid sculpts a jagged hole in a block of ice. Some of the water molecules immediately disperse to form an invisible gas, then quickly cool and condense into tiny water droplets that make up the cloud of mist rising above the ice block. Whenever water takes the form of ice, some liquid and gas are always present.

An Ironclad Molecular Bond

Hydrogen and oxygen have so great an affinity for one another that, given even the slightest nudge, they come together violently, forming water and releasing great quantities of energy. In 1937 the huge dirigible *Hindenburg* exploded over Lakehurst, New Jersey, when its hydrogen, ignited by a spark, fused with the oxygen in the air; amid the explosive release of energy, water was produced.

Conversely, it takes a great deal of energy to split water into its components. In fact, in ancient times water was considered a basic, indestructible element of the universe. Not until Henry Cavendish startled the scientific community in 1783 by synthesizing the water molecule did it become clear that the substance is actually a compound made up of one part oxygen and two parts hydrogen.

The reason water was long thought to be a single element was that the sturdy water molecule remains intact even when frozen solid or heated to temperatures at which many other compounds disintegrate. For the atoms of the water molecule are laced together by powerful bonds (*below*), which can be severed only by the most aggressive agents—such as electrical energy or certain chemicals. One such chemical is potassium; when even a small lump of potassium is dropped into water, it pulls the molecules apart so violently that the container of water may actually explode.

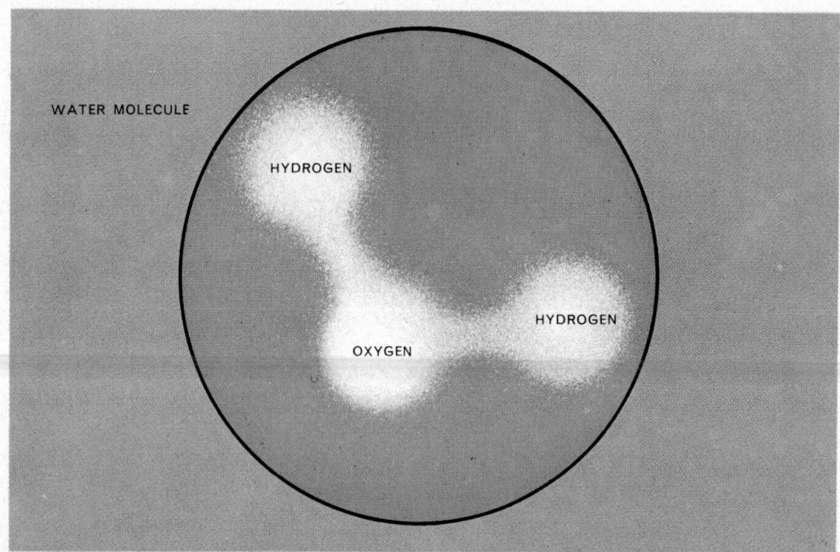

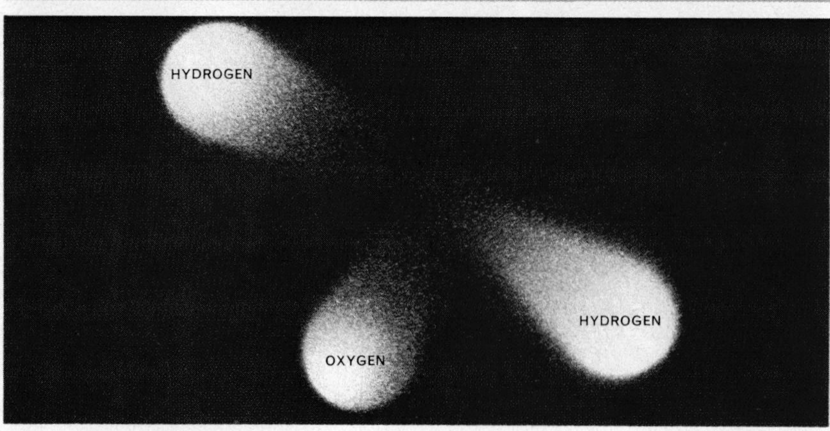

THE KEY TO STABILITY
Water's unique character is a result of the bonds that tie its two elements together. The way in which an oxygen atom is linked to two hydrogen atoms to form water is shown above. The couplings of their atomic particles are akin to keys slipping into locks; the fit is so perfect that water is one of nature's most stable compounds. When these bonds between elements are broken by electrical energy or chemicals (*bottom*), the oxygen and hydrogen regain their separate identities and are free to seek alliances with other elements, creating new compounds.

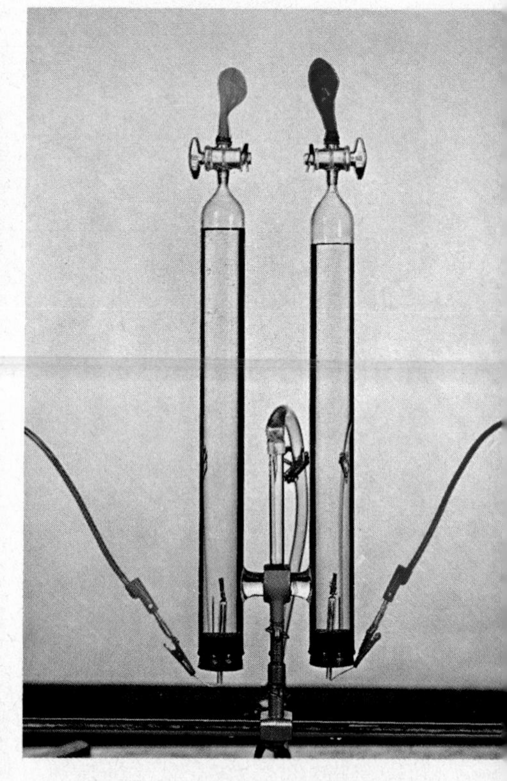

SPLITTING THE WATER MOLECULE
Splitting the water molecule with electricity is a traditional laboratory demonstration. The two columns of liquid water in the picture above almost fill their respective tubes. The balloons attached to the top of the tubes are deflated. When the current is turned on (*right*), oxygen atoms break away at the positive terminal, or blue wire, and bubble upwards into the blue balloon. Hydrogen atoms are released at the negative terminal, the red wire, and rise into the red balloon. Because two hydrogen atoms are released for every oxygen atom, the red balloon inflates twice as fast. Using standard household current, it would take about 10 years to disintegrate a bath full of water.

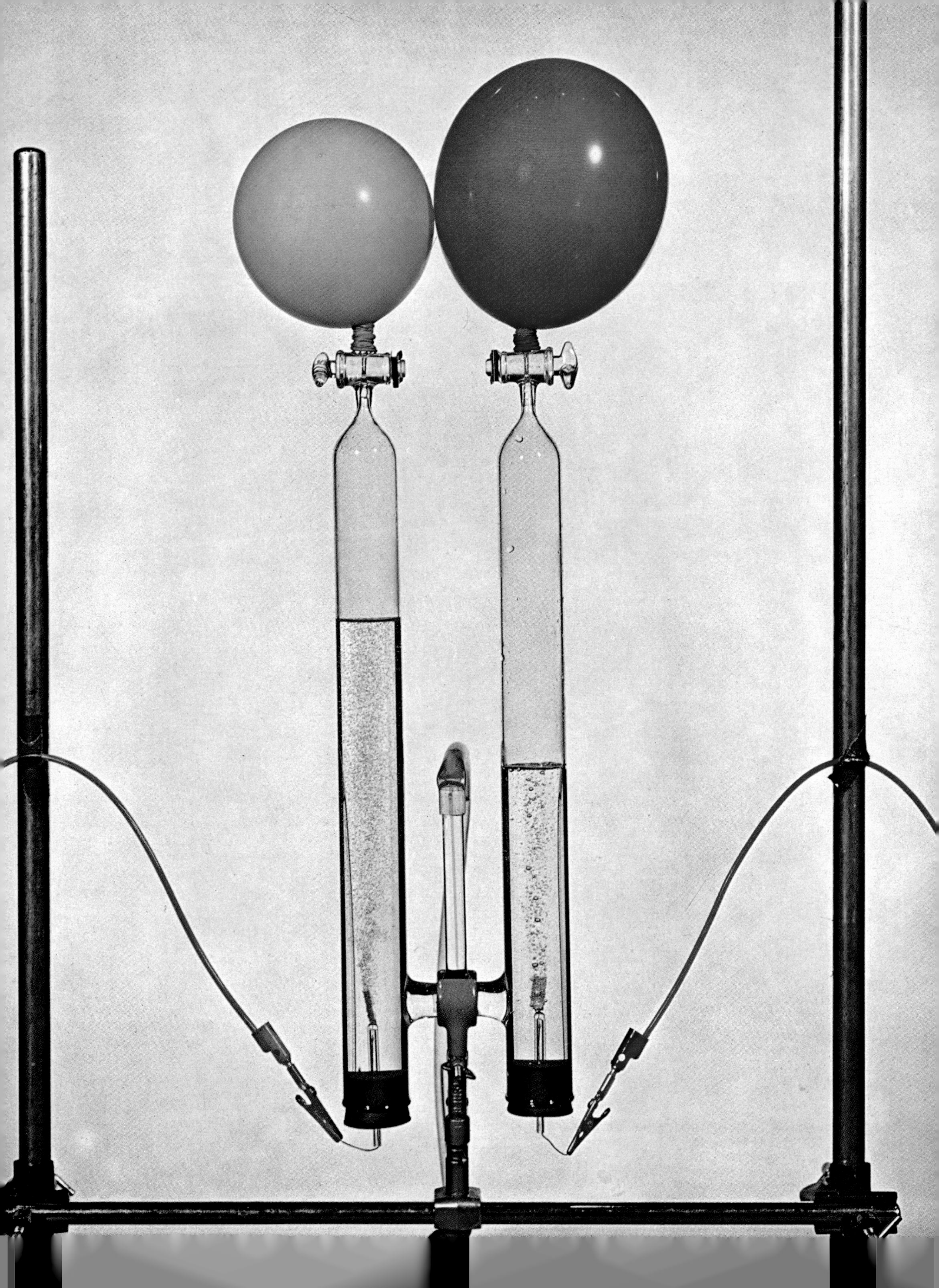

A Network of Nimble Molecules

Once formed, water molecules join with one another in a unique way, creating the liquid latticework shown in the diagram at the far right. The connection between water molecules is called a hydrogen bond. When water is in the form of ice, these bonds hold the molecules in a more or less rigid pattern. But in a liquid state this structure gives way to a chaotic molecular square dance in which groups of molecules take turns whirling about with one another, breaking their bonds, and finding new groups to form partners with.

When water is heated the pace increases until the bonds, no longer able to keep their partners at arm's length, snap, and the molecules fly off as gas. It is these bonds that pull water's surface into a taut sheet—a phenomenon known as surface tension.

A DROP TAKES SHAPE
A water-drop, shown above forming on the lip of a tap, is given its shape by the hydrogen bonds pulling its molecules inwards towards the centre of the drop—one manifestation of surface tension. Due to the force of gravity, the drop initially takes a tear shape; it becomes spherical as it falls, and ultimately flattens out before hitting the sink because of air resistance.

THE TIES THAT BIND

In a liquid state a water molecule can establish hydrogen bonds with four of its immediate neighbours (*right*) except at the surface, where there are no water molecules above it. As is shown in the diagram at the far right, surface molecules form bonds only below and to the sides.

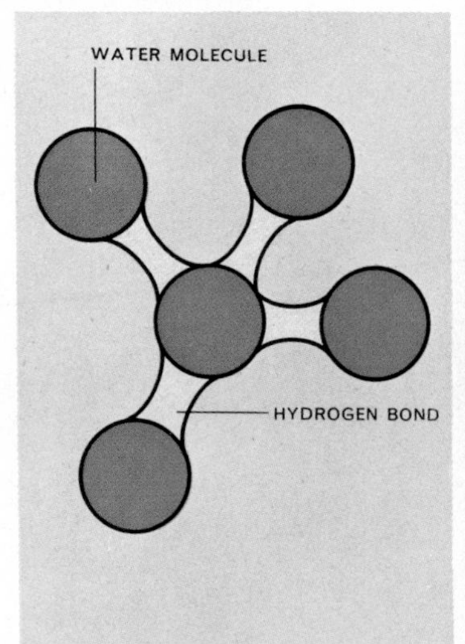

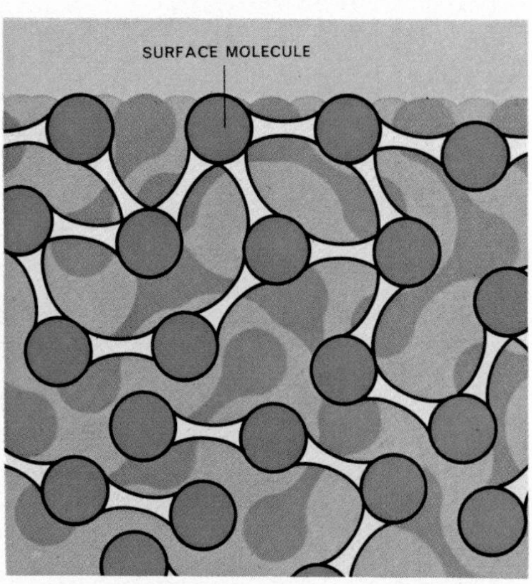

A WEIGHT AFLOAT

The surface of the water in a tumbler can support amazing weight—in this case a heavy metal grid—if the object is flat enough to take full advantage of surface tension. If the grid had been placed in the water edge first, however, its weight would have been concentrated on too few hydrogen bonds, and it would have sunk.

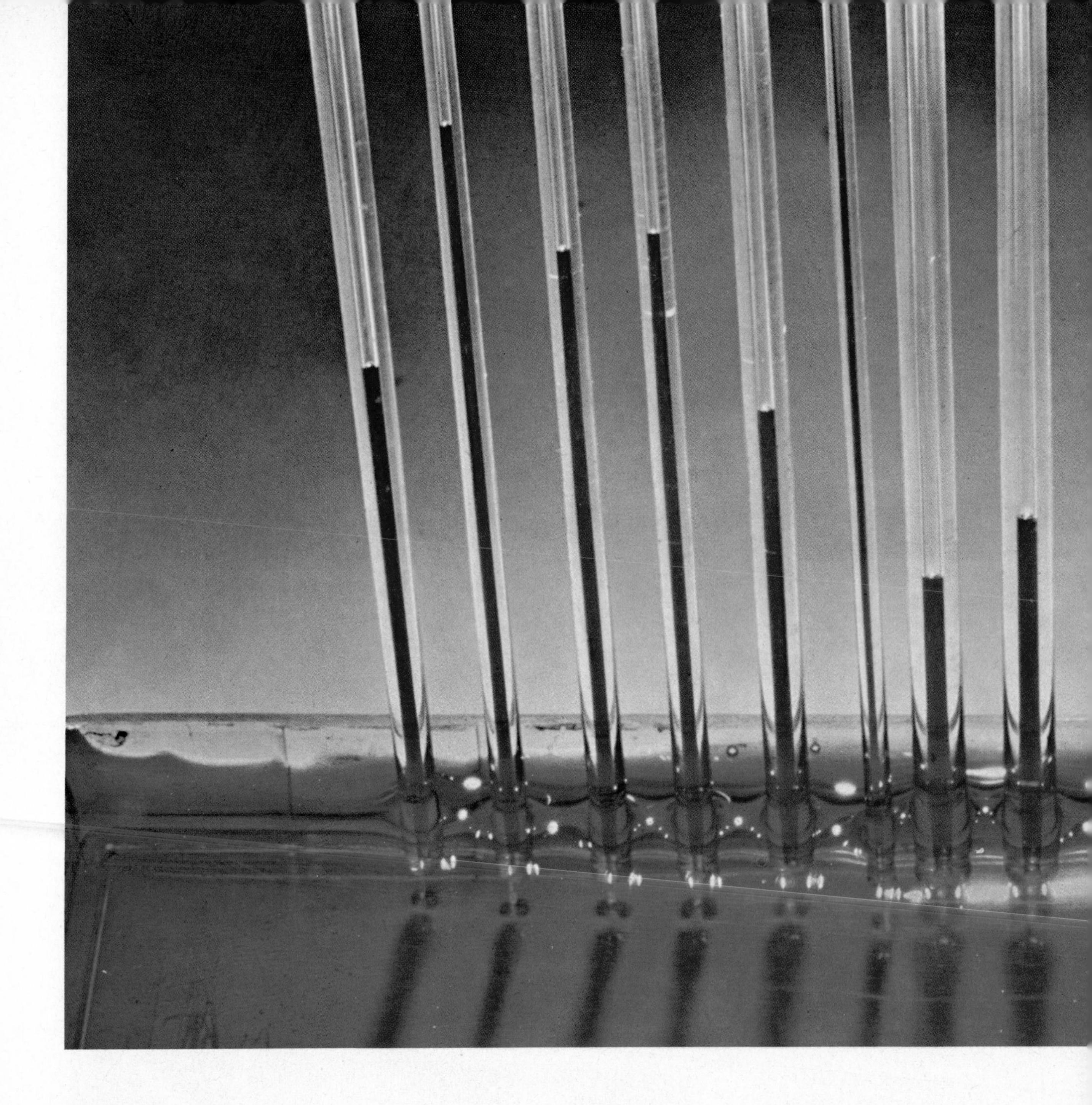

The Climbing Molecules

Water's bag of tricks bulges with surprises. One of these is water's ability to creep uphill under certain conditions. Without this characteristic, known as capillary action, the flow of nutriments to plants and trees would stall in the soil, and blood, which is largely water, would have great difficulty completing its circuit of the body.

The explanation for this phenomenon lies in the nature of water molecules. Bound to each other in almost every direction, they also bind to a variety of other substances, such as glass, clay or soil. In fact, almost any solid that has oxygen in it will lure the hydrogen in water. Thus, the surface of the dyed water in the tubes above is like a chain made up of hydrogen links. When the molecules at the edge reach for and adhere to the molecules of glass just above them, they haul the rest of the chain along with them. The surface, in turn, pulls the entire body of water to a new level. The molecules at the edge now repeat the process, and the water smoothly continues its ascent. It ends only when the downward pull of gravity is too great to overcome.

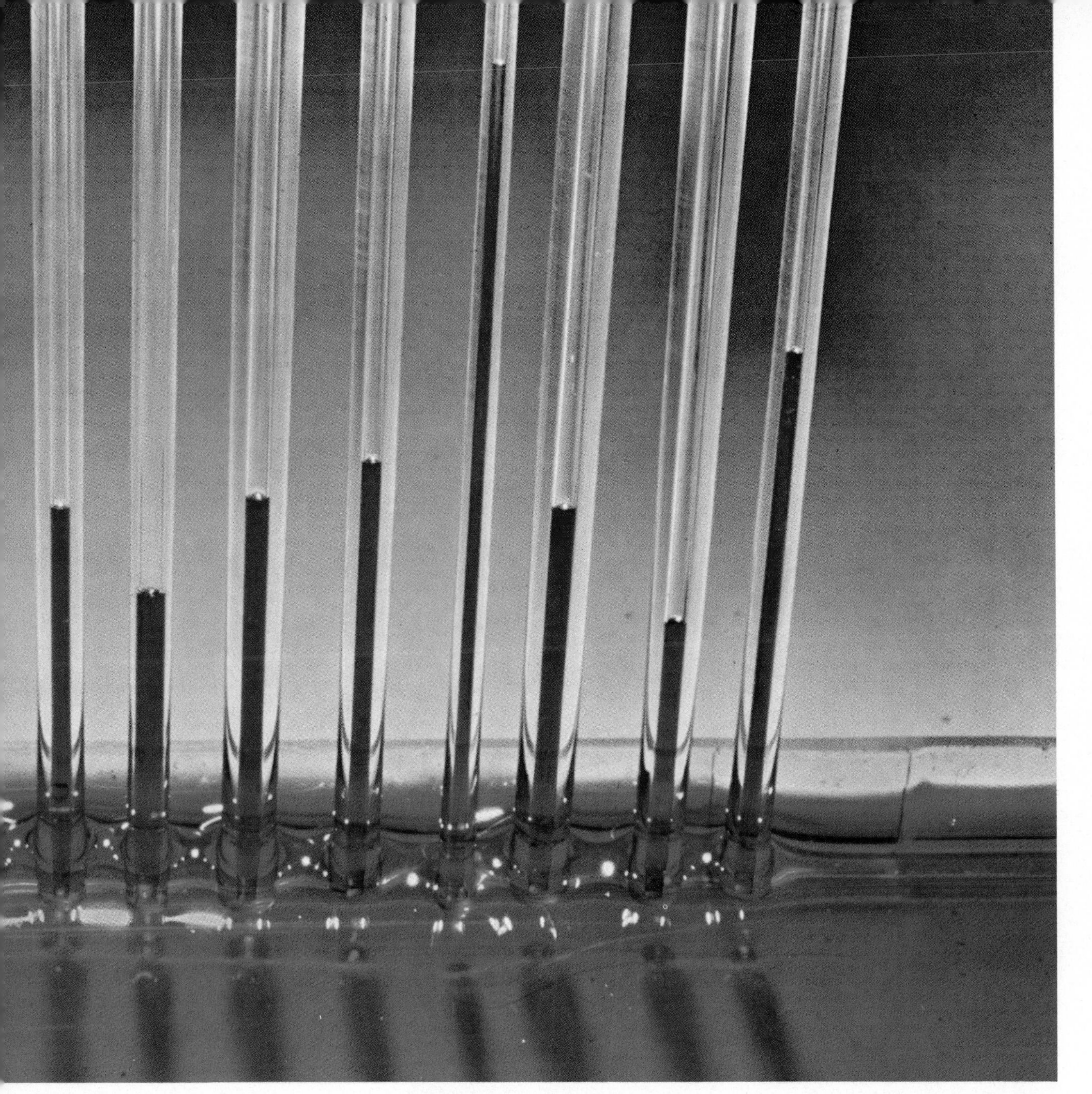

CLIMBING IN COLUMNS
Rising by capillary action, water slowly ascends in a series of tubes. It reaches higher levels in the narrower tubes, which contain less water for each molecule at the edge to lift. Doubling the diameter of the tube adds twice the edge for the molecules to adhere to—but it also adds four times as much water to be raised.

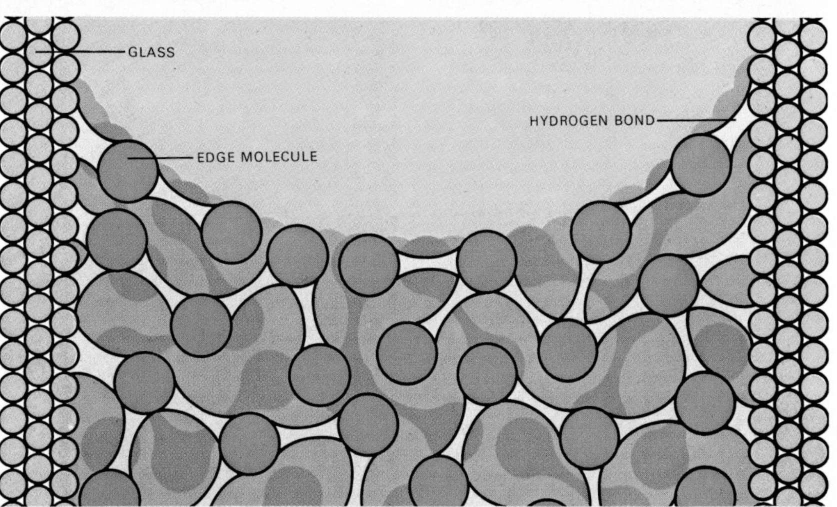

CLAMBERING UP THE EDGE
Attracted by the oxygen atoms in glass, water molecules adhere to the sides of a glass tube, stretching the surface into a crescent shape. As indicated by the network of hydrogen bonds, the edge molecules pull the others with them.

The Universal Solvent

Water is close to being the all-purpose chemical solvent: given enough time, it will dissolve almost any inorganic substance. In fact, about half of the known elements are found dissolved in the earth's waters.

Without water's property of solubility, nutrition could not go on: all living organisms depend on water to dissolve the substances they feed on. The roots of plants cannot absorb food in the soil unless it is in solution, and humans' food must be dissolved before it can enter the blood-stream.

Water molecules in contact with foreign substances act like cowboys cutting cattle from a herd—they force their way between clusters of particles, break them apart and hold them at bay. Water's capacity for such action is staggering: a gallon of water (ten pounds) dissolves 84 pounds of the fertilizer ammonium nitrate.

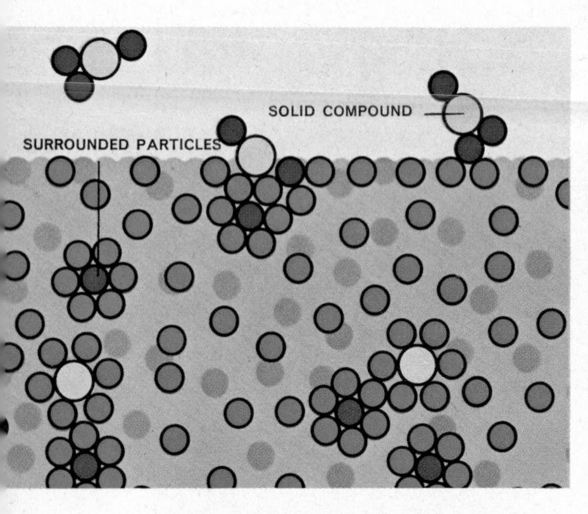

PICKING A SUBSTANCE APART
A solid compound (*purple*) dropped into liquid water is quickly broken up by water molecules (*blue*), which squeeze between the solid particles, separate them from one another and surround the liberated particles with a protective shield that prevents them from regrouping.

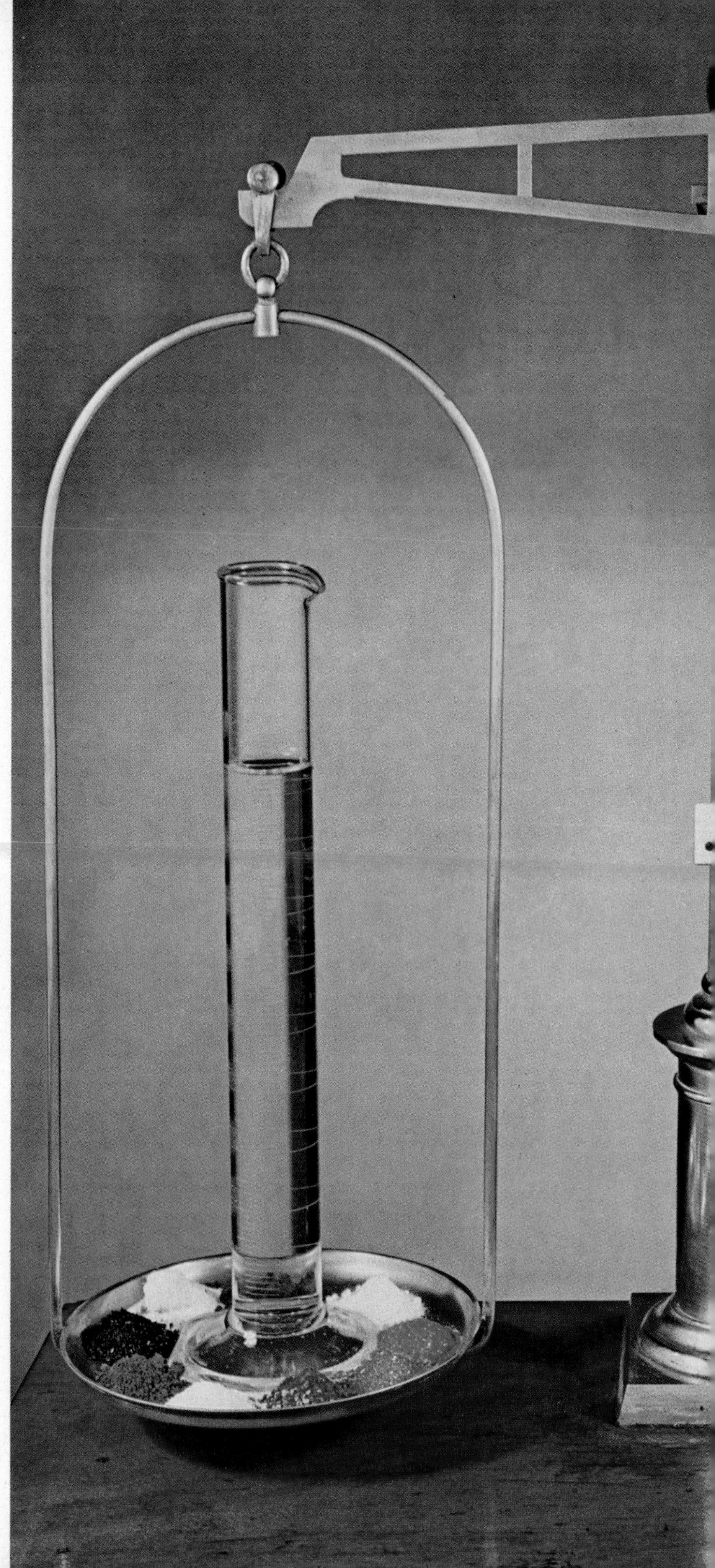

A TUBE THAT NEVER FILLS
Each tray of this scale holds a test tube of water plus six chemicals, but in one case the chemicals have been added to the water. Since the amounts of chemicals are equal, the trays balance—but, surprisingly, the volume of water on the right is not increased by the added matter.

A SOLID IN SOLUTION
A granulated solid disintegrates as its surface molecules, broken away from the main body, are surrounded by molecules of water. As water attacks the solid in this fashion, streamers of dissolving particles appear and the solid then changes its state as surely as if it were melted.

Equipping Water to Carry Current

There is a good chance that a man who plugs his electric razor into a socket while standing in the bath will receive a walloping jolt of current. Yet, oddly enough, water itself is a very poor conductor of electricity; in fact, no current at all can pass through it when it is pure and distilled. But when there are impurities in water —as is most often the case—the liquid is endowed with the properties it needs to conduct electricity.

The reason is that electric current requires free charged particles to carry it through a medium such as water. These particles (usually traces of dissolved salts) are abundant in impure water. In distilled water the atoms of oxygen and hydrogen are so perfectly fitted together that such particles do not exist.

The experiment shown below demonstrates how water is transformed into a conductor. In the beaker on the left, distilled water has been substituted for a length of wire that would complete an electric circuit. Since there are no free charged particles in the water, the electric energy is halted and cannot complete its journey to the light bulb. When impurities are added (*centre and right*), the electric energy has the material it needs to bridge the gap between the two terminals. The impurities break down as they dissolve, providing free charged particles. Set in motion by the electric energy, they complete the circuit.

To complete an electric circuit, current must pass through the water between the two wires in the beaker (*left*). When salt (shown dyed)

ELECTRIFYING WATER
The three panels on the right illustrate the way impurities increase water's capacity to conduct electricity, as shown in the photographs below. On the left are pure water molecules. At the centre salt crystals are introduced. They immediately dissolve, yielding ions, or particles, of sodium (*tan*) and chlorine (*yellow*), which are encircled by water molecules. As indicated by the arrows, the negatively charged chlorine ions head for the positive terminal; the positively charged sodium heads for the negative terminal. As more salt is added (*right*), more ions are set in motion.

SALT CRYSTALS
– +
CHLORINE ION
SODIUM ION

NO CURRENT | WEAK CURRENT | STRONG CURRENT

is added (*centre*) to provide carriers, the current can flow and light the bulb. More salt (*right*) produces more current and a brighter glow.

A Light-Weight among Solids

Water, which often appears to follow a set of natural laws all its own, behaves most outlandishly when it forms ice. For one thing, unlike most other compounds, it is lighter in this solid form than it is as a liquid. As a result, it floats when it freezes. If this did not happen in nature and ice were heavier than water, it would continuously sink to the bottom, where the sun's rays could not melt it. Slowly an ice pack would build upwards until the world's oceans, rivers and lakes became frozen solid.

Even as it changes from a liquid to a solid, water acts contrary to expectations. At first it follows the universal pattern of cooling: it contracts, and grows heavier and more dense. But when cooled below 4° C. it suddenly begins to expand and grow lighter and less dense. The reason for this odd change lies, again, in the hydrogen bonds that exist between water molecules. As they cool, the molecules slow up and begin crowding together. At 0° C., the bonds bring them to a halt and fix them at arm's length from one another in light-weight crystals of ice.

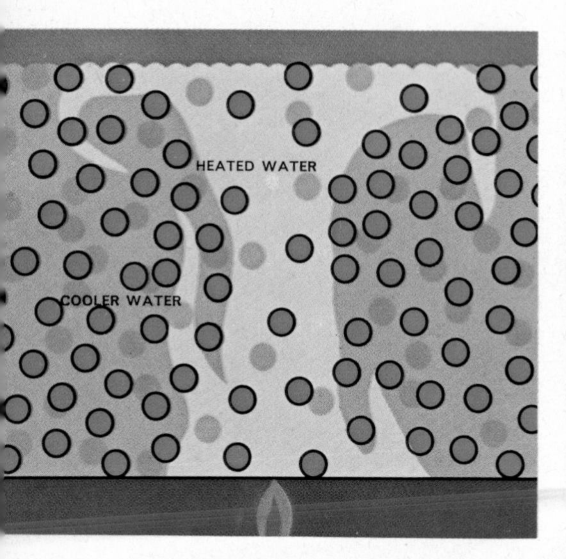

THE PATTERN OF DENSITY
As with any liquid, molecules of heated water (*yellow area above*) are considerably less dense than cooler molecules. Yet the most extreme differences in water density occur within a degree of each other: the least dense water molecules are those in ice (*white, below*); the most dense are those in the streamers of extremely cold water (*brown*), freshly melted out of ice.

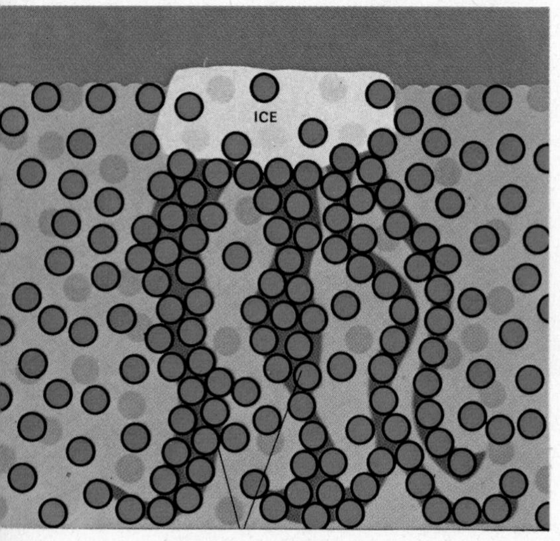

A RISE TO THE TOP
Heated from below by a Bunsen burner, water at the bottom of a tank grows lighter and quickly rises to the top. But as it rises, moving farther away from the source of heat, it immediately begins to cool. When it reaches the surface, the warmer water behind it nudges it out of the way. Still cooling and becoming more dense, the water falls, creating a circular flow.

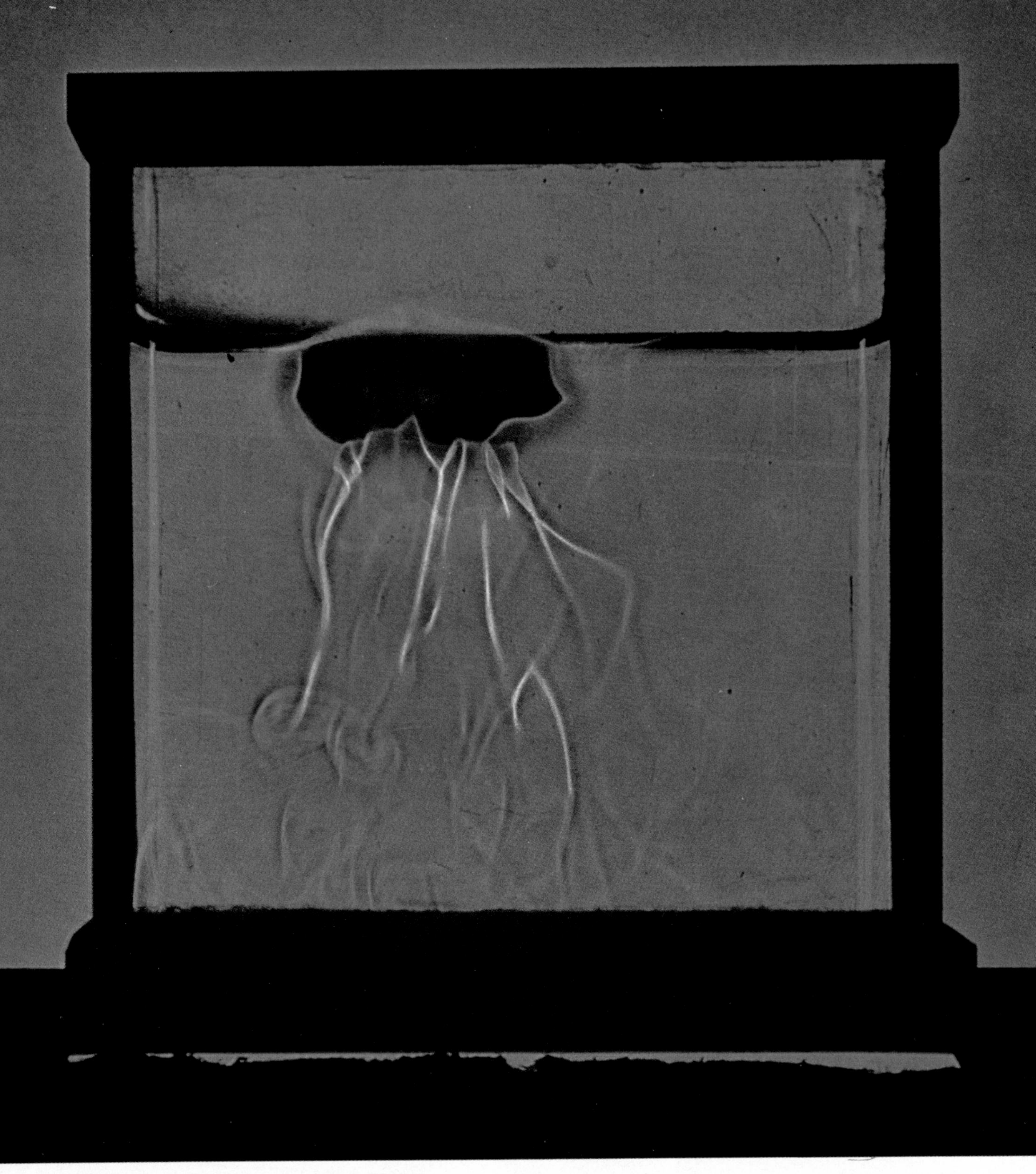

A DROP TO THE BOTTOM

A piece of ice, lighter and less dense than liquid water, floats on the surface of a water tank. But as the ice melts, relinquishing its airy crystalline structure, it becomes more dense and forms the streamers shown radiating from the ice block. This brief period of great density occurs because as ice melts, the hydrogen bonds between molecules begin to collapse and the molecules crowd closely together. At 4° C. they reach maximum density. Above 4° C. the heat sets the molecules moving more rapidly and the water expands and becomes lighter.

A Compound Slow to Boil

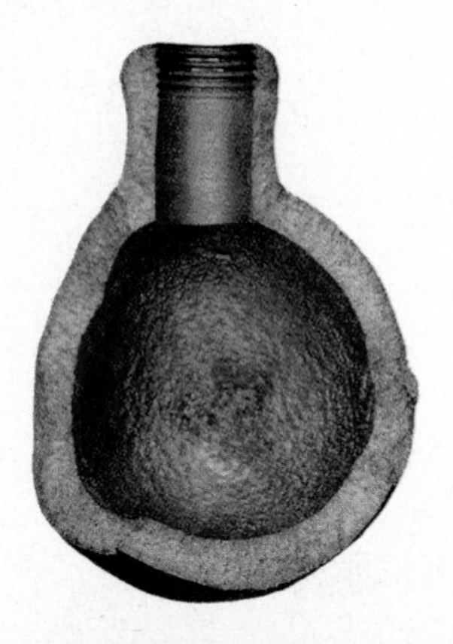

Householders whose water pipes have burst when the temperature suddenly fell need no other proof that water, unlike most liquids, releases tremendous energy when it freezes. Conversely, it must absorb a great deal of energy—in the form of heat—before its temperature is raised even slightly. An iron kettle used to boil water will be blistering hot long before the water in it is lukewarm. This property accounts for water's use as a cooling agent in car engines: it soaks up an enormous amount of heat without boiling.

In this manner, large bodies of water and the moisture in the atmosphere can regulate extremes of temperature, absorbing heat on hot days, and giving off heat on cold days. Where there is little natural water, as on the desert, temperatures can range from a searing 50° C. to well below freezing at night.

Before the temperature of a substance can be raised, its molecules must be prodded into vigorous motion. But in water molecules, the firm grip of the hydrogen bonds must first be loosened—a task which requires considerable amounts of heat. If the hydrogen bonds did not put up such firm resistance, water would boil at temperatures lower than those at the North Pole, and all the world's water would immediately evaporate.

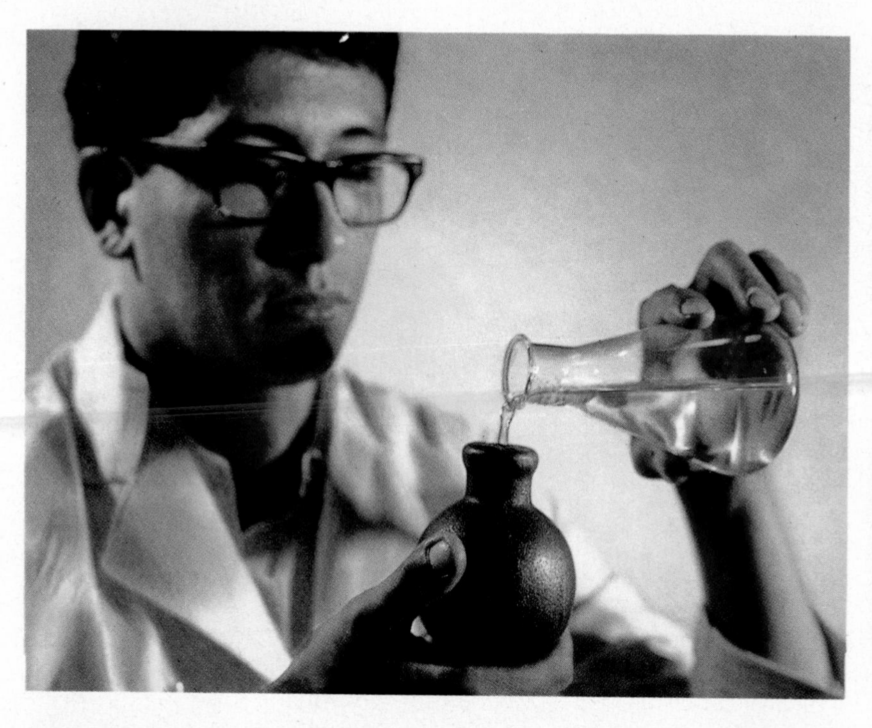

THE FORCE OF FREEZING
A violent explosion (*right*) can occur when water is frozen in a confined space. A quarter-inch-thick cast-iron container—shown in cross-section at the top of the page—is filled with water (*above, left*) and placed in a beaker of dry ice and alcohol (*above*). As the water freezes and expands, a tremendous amount of energy is exerted against the walls of the container. Finally the container explodes, hurling some fragments deep into a steel door 20 feet away

LIQUID WATER

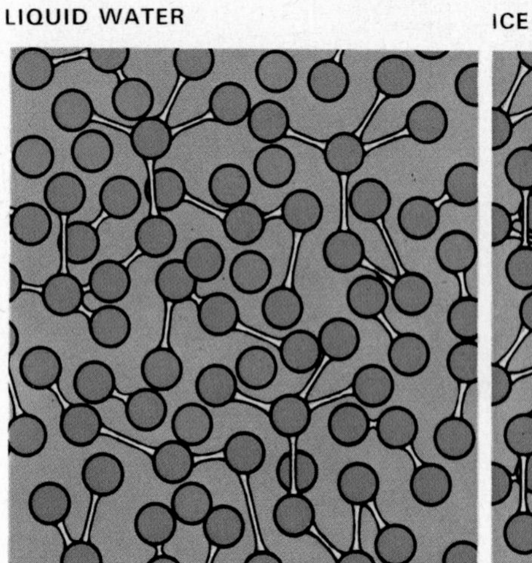

ICE

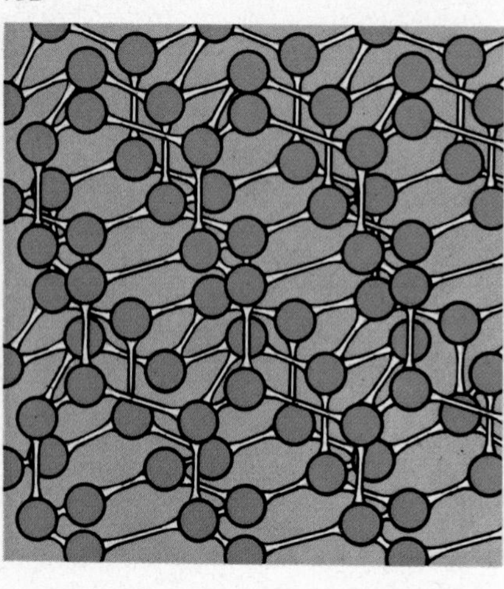

THE ARCHITECTURE OF ICE
The water molecules in ice (*left*) are held in a relatively rigid geometric pattern by their hydrogen bonds, producing an open, porous structure. In liquid water (*far, left*), which has fewer bonds, more molecules can occupy the same space, making liquid water more dense than ice.

2

A Sun-Powered Cycle

THE CYCLE IN ACTION: GEMINI V's CAMERA CATCHES AN ATLANTIC STORM SWEEPING TOWARDS MOROCCO'S COAST.

Among the nine planets, the earth is uniquely endowed with large quantities of water in its liquid state. The world supply of 326 million cubic miles of this substance would, if poured upon, say, Australia, submerge that country to a depth of over 100 miles. Equal in importance to the quantity is the earth's ability to maintain it in all three of the fundamental states of matter—i.e., as a liquid, solid and vapour. Water is the only common material that exists naturally in all three states on earth and the earth is apparently the only planet in the solar system that sustains water in this way. The circumstance has not only determined the course of life on earth but may have limited life, within this solar system, to earth alone.

For thousands of years, men have recognized—sometimes dimly, sometimes clearly—the significance of water's role. So abundant, so unusual, so essential is it that it has never failed to stimulate wonder. Man is himself a porous sac of water; only one-third of his body by weight is composed of other compounds. Water provides the surging oceans, the mist from a marsh, the creeping glacier, the volcano's explosive steam, a snowball, the 5,000 million tons or more of moisture that may be whirled through the air by a small hurricane.

This bewildering variety tells something of water's restless nature. It is never still. The apparently inert tumblerful of water may simultaneously convert ice cubes into liquid, release tiny amounts of vapour into the air above it, and condense vapour into droplets on its smooth glass sides. This is the fidgety world of water in microcosm. Projected on to a grand global scale, all 326 million cubic miles of this active substance are constantly responding to a complex of mighty natural forces—the rotation of the earth, the radiant heat of the sun, and the gravitational effects of the earth and its companions in the solar system. Added to these forces are the effects of surface irregularities—the mountains, valleys and plains on the continents and the oceans' basins—plus the chemistry and texture of terrestrial matter. Each contributes to a dynamic and perpetual metamorphosis—the shifting, changing, fickle nature of gaseous, solid and liquid water.

In one vitally important respect, however, water's behaviour is steadfast: the total supply neither grows nor diminishes. It is believed to be almost precisely the same now as it was 3,000 million years ago. Endlessly recycled, water is used, disposed of, purified and used again. Last night's potatoes may have been boiled in what was, ages ago, the bath water of Archimedes. And while the idea of using "used" water may at first repel an hygienic civilization, the knowledge that the world supply of this vital substance cannot be depleted should offer comfort.

The durability of water raises the question of whether it has existed always. What, indeed, was the source of all water in the shadowy beginnings of the young and lifeless earth? Modern scientists see a direct connection to a grander puzzle, the origin of the earth itself. The occurrence and nature of water are clearly related to the size of our planet, to its position in the heavens, and its formation.

The most widely accepted theory of the origin of the earth was developed in 1944 by the German theoretician Carl F. von Weizsäcker, and later modified by Gerard P. Kuiper of the University of Arizona. It proposes that the sun evolved from a vast gaseous cloud of hydrogen and helium. Scattered throughout this cloud in the form of fine dust, and comprising about 1 per cent of the whole, were the elements and compounds of which the planets are made. Water—in the form of vapour and crystals—was one of these compounds.

As this cosmic cloud spun about in space, gravitation—the mutual attraction of the particles for one another—caused a core area to form and to contract. As the density of the core increased, its temperature also increased, finally reaching that level, high almost beyond imagining (about 12,500,000° C.), at which hydrogen nuclei fuse into helium and release energy. Thus began the thermonuclear reaction that is the self-sustaining source of the sun's heat and light.

The earth's watery nature

The sun condensed into a separate body before it had drawn all the near-by cosmic cloud into itself. What remained continued to whirl about as huge eddying discs of colliding particles that formed ever-larger aggregates of matter. After several million years they became the nine identifiable members of the family of planets. The water that was part of the original cloud became part of each, in an amount and condition that depended both upon the planet's mass (which determines its gravitational attraction) and upon its distance from the sun (which determines the planet's surface temperature).

The earth's watery nature results entirely from its middling size and middling position. It is massive enough for its gravitational force to hold an atmosphere of water vapour and other heavy gases. Its position 93 million miles from the sun keeps it near the centre of a narrow zone where temperatures permit water to exist as liquid, solid and vapour. This zone, as distances in the cosmos are reckoned, is extremely narrow: 10 million miles, about one-tenth the radius of the earth's orbit. Only the earth can fit in such a limited zone, and only the earth seems likely to contain the three natural states of water.

The best way to appreciate earth's good fortune is by examining its nearest neighbours, Mars and Venus, which lie just outside the three-state zone. The Mariner space craft that came within 2,130 miles of the Martian surface registered evidence of an airless and cold planet, too cold for liquid water. There is some water vapour which could form directly from ice. And there may indeed be traces of ice mixed with the frozen carbon dioxide that covers Mars' polar caps and gives them their characteristic light appearance.

Venus, though closest to earth, remains the most difficult planet to investigate, for its opaque atmosphere prevents visual study of what goes on beneath. Radio waves do penetrate the cloud cover, however, and indicate a surface temperature of about 450° C., too high for ice or liquid water there. Some water may exist as part of the atmospheric cloud, which seems to be mainly carbon dioxide. But whether this water exists as liquid droplets or ice crystals is a matter of controversy among astronomers.

Beyond Venus, towards the sun, only tiny Mercury orbits. Recent radio observation of Mercury reveals that the planet rotates on its axis one and a half times for every orbit round the sun. The blistering heat (410°C.) of the sunny side exceeds the melting point of lead (327°C.), while the temperature of the dark side is −174°C. Such water as Mercury has must be trapped in the cold crust of the polar areas; there is no possibility of surface water nor of an atmosphere. Mercury's small mass does not produce enough gravitational force to prevent the escape of gas into space.

From Mars out to the farthest reaches of the solar system, the temperature drops below −180°C. as the distance from the sun increases. All surface water on planets beyond Mars is therefore frozen. Pluto, the most distant, is small, but Saturn, Neptune and Uranus are giant planets and likely to possess quantities of water commensurate with their mass. Jupiter, a large planet with many features of a star, is the exception; its atmosphere may be warm enough to contain water droplets.

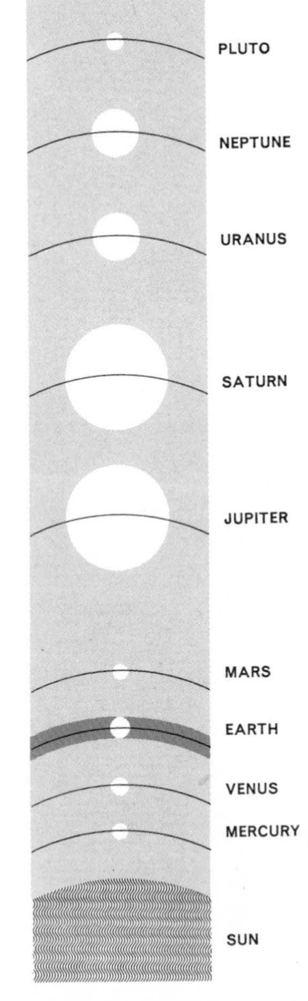

IN THE SOLAR SYSTEM, water in all three of its forms—ice, vapour and liquid—is found on a planetary surface only in the narrow ring (dark blue) that includes the earth's orbit. Closer to the sun, there is apparently no liquid water on the surfaces, although Venus's atmosphere may contain vapour or ice. Farther from the sun, any surface water must be frozen, although some rain may appear briefly within the deep atmosphere of the huge planet Jupiter. Since liquid water is essential to the living processes now known, the earth seems to be the only planet capable of supporting life.

Oceans, glaciers and air

Included in the cosmic dust when clumping formed the earth were the constituents of the water we use today. How those molecules were transformed into oceans of liquid, glaciers of ice and humid atmosphere is a subject of debate. Two theories have been suggested, competitive parts of over-all theories which attempt to explain the steps in the evolution of the planet. The most widely accepted of them holds that the formative earth heated up—from the impact of additional meteor-like matter from space; from radioactivity, then 15 times as great as now; and from the increase in pressure as gravity compacted the original material. According to this theory the earth grew so hot, in fact, that it melted, first in its centre, and finally, after 100 million years or so, throughout. The water supply vaporized and then, since water molecules at very high temperatures decompose chemically into their constituent hydrogen and oxygen atoms, it disappeared. While water as such no longer existed, the possibility of water remained, as the gases swirled within and above the turbulent surface of the molten planet.

When the radioactivity declined and the compaction process slowed down, the temperature cycle reversed. The earth gradually cooled. Before its crust solidified, most of the atmosphere of hot gases was lost; it simply boiled away into space. This was replaced with exhalation from inside the earth, including water vapour. As the vapour steamed up from fissures and craters and bursting bubbles of viscous rock to condense in the cold of the upper atmosphere, it curtained the earth with a dense, thick cloud of water droplets and snow.

As the earth cooled further, according to the theory, the water in the air approached nearer the surface until, finally, the earth was cool enough for water to be able to strike ground without immediately evaporating. Then began a deluge that continued for centuries. When the cloud mantle thinned sufficiently, the sun lighted and warmed the surface waters, the primeval seas that were eventually to bear life.

This version of the earth's birth has been disputed by some authorities, Nobel laureate Harold C. Urey among them. Urey suggested that the earth was never completely molten, but rather was born cold and has retained a cool, solid crust ever since. The water, he believed, emerged gradually from this crust instead of raining down in a great deluge.

This theory was based on the fact that the original cosmic dust, compacting into the rocks of the planet, could have trapped water molecules inside their crystalline structure. The crust of the earth is today largely silicate rock—hydrated crystals which contain water molecules integrated into their atomic arrangements. The water can be driven out of such hydrated crystals rather easily by heat. If the earth had been born cold, as the Urey theory maintained, this water of hydration existed from the beginning; it was released later in local areas by intermittent heating, which could have been caused by the collisions between large chunks of matter and the growing earth. Still later, the heat from volcanic activity and meteorite impacts would have boiled additional water of hydration from rocks inside the earth.

The slow growth of the seas

Thus, over long periods of time, water may have accumulated in pools on the surface of the earth. A slow growth of the oceans would explain why they are no more salty now than they apparently were hundreds of millions of years ago, despite the fact that whole continents have been washed into them. If the oceans have always been their present size, the addition of so much other material should have tended to increase their saltiness progressively.

The two theories agree about one thing: the oceans, whether they were created suddenly by a deluge or gradually by the dehydration of rocks, filled basins that already existed. These basins are themselves remarkable—the Pacific deeper than any mountain is high, its floor gaping with chasms; the Atlantic, shallower, seamed by a submerged mountain chain, edged with shorelines that seem to meet.

The origin of the basins, however, is also in dispute. A number of proposals have been advanced. Urey suggested that they were gouged out of the solid earth by space materials crashing into the planet. A more dramatic but now discredited view held that the Pacific basin is the hole left behind when the moon was torn free from the earth. That idea was given up when scientists got a chance of examining the rocks the astronauts brought back from their lunar explorations. The moon rocks proved to be totally different from—and much older than—any found on earth. Clearly the moon could never have been part of the earth.

Hardly less fantastic is a view of the ocean basis now so buttressed by evidence that it is generally accepted as providing the true explanation for their origin. According to this theory, viscous material driven by convection currents beneath the earth's crust continuously seeps up through the crust, mainly from a global crack that runs along the crest of a 40,000-mile-long mountain range girdling the earth on the ocean floor. The upsurging material quickly hardens and pushes the earth's crust sideways in both directions, east and west. A similar phenomenon can take place beneath a continent, splitting it in two and separating the pieces. Between the pieces an ocean bed is formed. The moving crust piles up in some places, as large chunks of it, travelling in different directions, collide and force one on top of the other. In the course of this process, some coastal mountains are pried up while the lower moving sections of the sea floor are moved downwards, returning to the interior of the earth as they form the deep trenches of the abyss, such as the 1,600-mile-long, 34,876-foot-deep Tonga-Kermadec Trench in the southwestern Pacific and the 35,800-foot-deep Mariana Trench near the Philippine Islands.

However the ocean's hollows came to be, they caught nearly every drop of the water that later became available. Today almost all the water on earth is in the oceans—and "almost all" is close to being absolutely all: 97.2 per cent of the total volume. The usable fresh water above and in the ground accounts for less than two-thirds of 1 per cent of the total, as the illustration on page 38 shows.

Taken together, the oceans and the ice caps and glaciers comprise 99.35 per cent of the earth's total water. The remaining two-thirds of 1 per cent is apportioned to all of many other manifestations of water around the globe. Included in that small fraction are the waters of all the great rivers and lakes of the world, the inland seas, the streams, springs, brooks and ponds, the pools and puddles, swamps and bogs, the rain, snow and vapour in the atmosphere, the water in pipes above and below the ground, in sewers and reservoirs, the snow and ice on mountain slopes, the moisture in the land and—most importantly—the ground-water that supplies the wells and helps to feed the streams and rivers. Ground-water, in part, accounts for about 97 per cent of that small usable supply, the water which remains when the oceans, ice caps and glaciers are subtracted from the world total.

A puzzle of distribution

The obvious disproportion in the distribution of water puzzled the ancients. In their view, rain and snow could not account for the quantity in lakes and streams, because not enough fell. Who, living in the arid region beside the Nile, could imagine that the river's annual flood derived from precipitation on mountains thousands of miles away? The men of other centuries also found it impossible to conceive of the ostensibly solid ground as an absorber and conveyer of rain; after all, digging into the earth produced water only in certain favoured spots. Until the 17th century, most men explained springs and deep well water in one of two ways: either it came from a vast underground reservoir, a fresh-water ocean hidden beneath crustal rock; or it moved from the sea through subterranean channels, was purified somehow, and then rose to pour out as springs or to lie in underground pools waiting to be tapped by wells. Of the two explanations, the former satisfied less; it ignored the need for replenishment of the underground storage.

The idea of a complete cycle—that water evaporated from the sea and land, was drawn into the atmosphere, fell as rain and snow, sank into the earth to reappear in watercourses, and then drained back into the sea—had attracted brilliant men over the years, but it could not be proved at that time and therefore was not generally accepted. With the development of modern science in the 16th and 17th centuries, however, attention was directed again and again to what seemed to be the cyclical pattern of all nature: Newton's law that for every action there must be a reaction, the recirculating blood system demonstrated by Harvey, the planetary orbits postulated by Copernicus. These rules of balance and repetition had been established by close observation and careful measurement. It was only natural, then, to seek a similar balance in the world's water supply and to seek it with similar techniques.

In the mid-17th century, two French scientists individually attacked the puzzle of the rivers. Each—Claude Perrault first and Edmé Mariotte a little later—measured the precipitation in the watershed of the Seine and then measured the river's rate of discharge, i.e., the amount of water it poured into the ocean in a given time. Their measurements, although crude, proved that, contrary to ancient belief, precipitation alone could account for the river's flow. Moreover, enough water would remain to supply the springs and wells. Mariotte went a step further; he showed that rain deeply infiltrated the ground wherever it fell, seeping downwards through porous soil until it reached impermeable material.

THE WORLD'S WATER SUPPLY

LOCATION	WATER VOLUME (Cubic miles)	PERCENTAGE OF TOTAL WATER
SURFACE WATER		
Freshwater lakes	30,000	.009
Saline lakes and inland seas	25,000	.008
Rivers and streams	300	.0001
	55,300	.017
SUBSURFACE WATER		
Soil moisture	16,000	.005
Ground-water within depth of half a mile	1,000,000	.31
Deep-lying ground-water	1,000,000	.31
	2,016,000	.625
ICE CAPS AND GLACIERS	7,000,000	2.15
ATMOSPHERE	3,100	.001
OCEANS	317,000,000	97.2
TOTALS (approximate)	326,000,000	100

WATER IS DISTRIBUTED in great or small amounts to every part of the earth. All but about 3 per cent of the water is held in oceans: the remainder is found as much as three miles under the earth's crust or (as vapour) as high as seven miles above the surface. The table above shows the quantity and percentage of water in all its habitats.

Halley's ingenious experiment

Another essential factor in the distribution cycle—the origin of rain and snow—remained to be proved. Shortly after Perrault and Mariotte completed their investigations, the English astronomer Edmund Halley showed that the earth's precipitation was of such magnitude that it could be balanced by evaporation: the evaporation from a large body of water was of an order of size equal to the amount it regained from the rivers that flowed into it. The key to Halley's discovery was the determination of the rate of evaporation. He used an ingenious but simple apparatus which he described in these words:

"We took a Pan of Water about 4 inches deep and 7 9/10 inches diameter, in which we placed a Thermometer, and by means of a Pan of Coals, we brought the Water to the same degree of heat which is observed to be that of the Air in our hottest Summers; the Thermometer nicely showing it. This done, we affixed the Pan of Water, with the Thermometer in it, to one end of the Beam of the Scales, and exactly counterpoised it with weights in the other Scale; and by the application or removal of the Pan of Coals, we found it very easie to maintain the Water in the same degree of Heat precisely."

From the loss in weight of his small pan of water, Halley could calculate the rate at which water evaporated at the temperature of "our hottest Summers". He then applied this rate to the estimated quantity of water in the Mediterranean and determined quite accurately how much evaporated from the large body of water. This he equated to the amount of water poured into the Mediterranean by rivers.

The concept of a hydrologic cycle unravelled the ancient riddle of water. Man could now understand that the water going out from the surface of the earth must come back in equal amount—a perpetual cycle with no beginning, middle or end. Maintaining this cycle requires that at any moment an average of 3,100 cubic miles of water must be distributed throughout the global atmosphere in the form of vapour or water droplets. While this may seem substantial, the amount is actually slight relative to the size of the atmosphere. If all of it abruptly fell as rain, the 3,100 cubic miles of water would cover the earth with barely an inch. The turnover is quite rapid; once ever 12 days, on the average, all the water in the air does fall and is subsequently replaced.

The statistics of circulation

About 95,000 cubic miles of water goes into the air annually. By far the greater part—approximately 80,000 cubic miles—rises from the ocean. But 15,000 cubic miles is drawn from the land, evaporated off lakes, streams and moist soil, and, most importantly, transpired from the leaf surfaces of living plants. The total process is called evapotranspiration.

Of the water that goes up into the atmosphere, most—71,000 cubic miles—falls back directly into the oceans. Another 9,000 cubic miles falls on land but runs off into rivers and streams and is returned to the oceans within days or, at most, a few weeks. The remaining 15,000 cubic miles soaks into the land and is available to participate in plant and animal life processes. In these processes too, water intake matches outgo as animal and vegetable life exhales, excretes and perspires what was earlier ingested through root and mouth.

While the hydrologic cycle balances what goes up with what comes down over the earth, no such reciprocity holds for individual areas. Wide differences occur in rates of both evaporation and precipitation.

Evaporation might be expected to be greatest at the equator, since the most solar energy strikes that area. But heavy clouds are more frequent over the equator than in most other regions; they reduce the radiation reaching the surface. And to the north and south, strong winds sweep up more moisture than the relatively calm winds of the equator. Winds play a critical role, for dry winds absorb more moisture than the winds of temperate areas. The highest evaporation rates on earth occur in the Red Sea and Persian Gulf, lying between 15° and 30° north latitude. The unmitigated ferocity with which sun and hot winds heat these bodies of water drives no fewer than 11½ feet a year from the Red Sea. One consequence is its extreme salinity.

Evaporation rates are still more variable on land; there is less exposed surface water, and the extremes of temperature and wind are greater. Some deserts have an evaporation rate of zero, because there is nothing to evaporate. In rain forests, on the other hand, the rate approximates that of the open ocean under the same conditions of wind and sunlight.

Drenching and drought

Precipitation varies even more than evaporation. Dramatic contrasts in rainfall and snowfall can be seen within a few miles on land—for example, Mount Waialeale in Hawaii receives an annual average of 460 inches, while 15 miles away, a rain gauge records only 18 inches in a year. Such variations result from topographic interference with the flow of wind over the earth's surface. Mountains prevent what might otherwise be a fairly uniform distribution, through precipitation, of the moisture carried by the wind. When a prevailing wind blows across the sea, or across land areas where the evaporation rate is high, it becomes loaded with moisture. Moving against a mountain-side, it is forced upwards and cooled so that its water vapour condenses to snow or rain. By the time it descends on the other side of the mountain, the once moist air, its water load squeezed from it, has become a desert wind. The effects of mountain barriers on patterns of wind and rain are called "orographic", which literally means "written by the mountains". Orographic effects, by definition, do not occur over the open sea, where precipitation is consequently much more even than on land.

Around the world, average annual rainfall ranges from below 10 to more than 40 inches—far from evenly distributed. In South America, for example, the effects of moisture-laden winds from the Pacific Ocean give parts of Colombia as much as 280 inches of rain a year. Farther south, however, the continual off-shore winds and the cool ocean provide a place such as Iquique, Chile, at the edge of the Atacama Desert, with an average of only half an inch a year.

The hydrologic cycle that averages out these local variations into a long-term global balance depends on the sun. The sun's radiant energy provides the power to raise water into the atmosphere so that it can fall again. The cycle resembles a steam-engine. In the hydrologic engine, the sun is the fire-box, the boiler is the ocean and the land, and the condenser is the cool upper atmosphere. This engine performs work on a grand scale: it makes weather, establishes climate, directs ocean currents, cuts valleys and builds deltas, and sustains life on land.

Much of this work involves, in one way or another, the transfer of heat around the earth. The water evaporating into the atmosphere enters the global system of prevailing winds. In the form of vapour and droplets, it travels thousands of miles before returning to the surface. In doing so, it carries heat in huge quantities around the globe and moderates the temperature extremes that would otherwise prevail.

The transfer of heat

As an example, consider what happens to water which has surfaced from the cold depths of the sea. If it rises in the tropics, it mixes with surface water which has a temperature of about 27° C. First of all, it helps to hold that temperature down. Evaporating from the surface, it is transformed from liquid into vapour, a change that requires energy. The water absorbs this energy as heat. The vapour can be considered a heat-carrying vehicle ready to travel the air currents flowing north and south from the equator. If the vapour enters the current high above the equator, the earth's rotation forces it to move north-easterly until it reaches a latitude of 30°. There, cooling, it may sink and slant across the North Temperate Zone to meet a cold air current from the Arctic. The joining of the disparate air masses results in a turbulent storm. The vapour abruptly condenses into liquid, and all the heat energy absorbed in the tropics is released and warms the frigid air. If in this process the liquid water freezes, it releases still more heat energy.

Water vapour is not the only means by which vast quantities of heat are transported from lower latitudes to higher, north and south of the equator. "Rivers" flow in the ocean; some are warm currents of water from the tropics and others are cold currents from the polar regions. These streams vary in width, volume and speed. The channels in which they flow are generally more stable than those on land, and they exert long-term influences on the environments of the earth's regions.

Scientists estimate that if the temperature difference between a warm current and the adjacent ocean is 11° C., every cubic mile of the current yields heat equal to that obtained by the efficient burning of six million tons of high-quality coal. It is as a result of one such vast heat exchange—that caused by the Atlantic's warm Gulf Stream—that the British Isles and parts of Norway enjoy a temperate climate while Labrador, at the same latitude on the western side of the Atlantic Ocean, is frigid.

Man's increasing knowledge of the hydrologic engine has answered many of the ancient riddles of water, but not all of them. We know where the rain comes from, yet we still cannot order its coming. We can explain why water fills the well, yet we still cannot always forecast correctly how much water any particular well will furnish. Today's attempts to control the great global engine are, like the incantations and dances of other times, merely attempts. Only new understanding, rising from an intensified study of water, may finally give man more effective influence over the bountiful compound that is essential to life on earth.

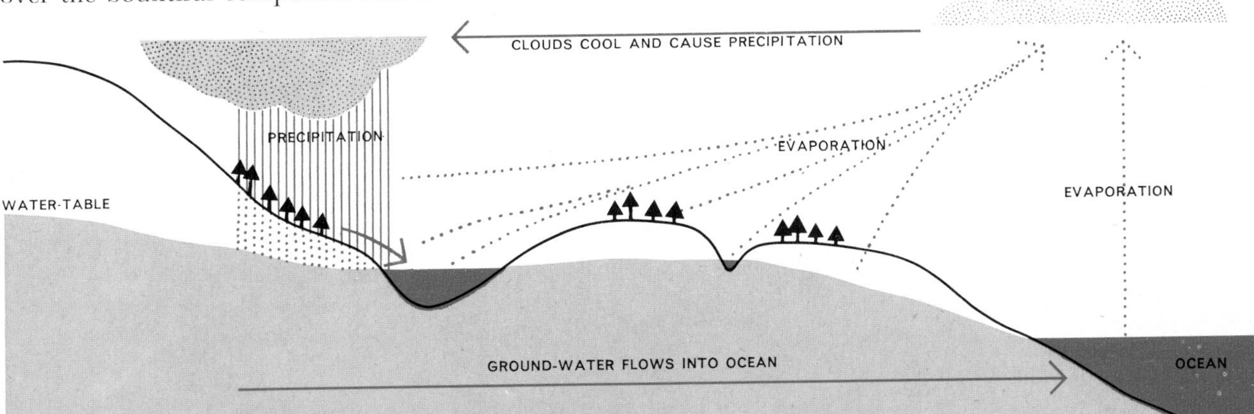

THE HYDROLOGIC CYCLE, the endless circulation of the earth's water, is pictured here, beginning on the left with precipitation of rain from a cloud. The rain sinks into the earth, some of the water eventually seeping into the ocean, some of it running into channels and lakes. Simultaneously it starts on the reverse stage of the cycle, evaporation (*dotted lines*). Some water actually evaporates during the rainfall; most of it rises from wet ground, from rivers and lakes, from the leaves of plants and above all from the ocean. The evaporated water collects in clouds; as these cool, precipitation occurs—and the cycle repeats itself.

The Long Voyage from Sea to Sea

The earth's original supply of water is still in use: little has been added or lost in the hundreds of millions of years since the first clouds formed and the first rains fell. The same water has been pumped time and again from the oceans into the air, dropped upon the land and transferred back to the sea. This process—the natural mechanism that evaporates ocean water, distributes it to every part of the earth, then returns it to the sea—is known as the hydrologic cycle. At any instant, only about 0.005 per cent of the total water supply is moving through the cycle; most of the water is stored in the oceans, frozen in glaciers, held in lakes or detained underground. A single drop of water spends 8 to 10 days passing through the air, 2 to 3 weeks in a river, as long as 100 years in an Alpine glacier, a few weeks to thousands of years in a lake, or in the ground from 100 to 40,000 years—or even longer. Eventually, however, every drop is moved on through the cycle. The hydrologic cycle uses more energy in a day than man has generated throughout history. But the cycle's machinery, powered by a constant input from the sun, has more energy than it can ever use.

DRAINING THE CYCLE
Flooding the Australian coastal flats, the river Norman winds past mangrove trees and empties into the South Pacific (*background*). Rivers are the drainpipes of the hydrologic cycle. The total number of rivers is practically uncountable—in the United States alone there are some three and a quarter million miles of river channel—yet rivers hold only 1/10,000 of the world's water.

Pumping Water from the Oceans

Every year more than 83,700 cubic miles of water is pumped out of the oceans by the hydrologic cycle. If the oceans were not constantly refilled, this water loss would lower their level by 39 inches a year. The "pump" of the cycle is the sun, which supplies energy to evaporate ocean water and release it into the air as vapour.

Actually, the hydrologic cycle is an extraordinarily inefficient machine. It utilizes only a small fraction of the solar energy available to it. Similarly, once a raindrop is deposited on a mountain-top, only about 5 per cent of its potential energy is used

in the work of erosion—95 per cent is converted to heat through friction as the water runs back into the sea. Yet the cycle, always supplied with more energy than it can use, operates like a perpetual motion machine. It is continually being reinvigorated by the prodigious force of the sun.

STOREHOUSE FOR THE CYCLE
The oceans, holding 317 million cubic miles of water, constitute 97.2 per cent of the earth's total supply. At the surface, countless sun-heated molecules are evaporated every minute, while a molecule at the bottom of the ocean may wait 2,000 years before it enters the cycle.

RELEASING THE RAINS
The driving rain of a midsummer thunderstorm pours tons of water on to the dusty plains of the western United States. The amount of precipitation varies along the cloud-bank. In the middle of the squall line (*bright area*) the rainfall is lighter. There heat radiated from the sunbaked earth evaporates raindrops almost as soon as they condense, and the ground remains dry.

SEQUEL TO A STORM
Sun shines through the scattering remnants of rain clouds, warming the earth and trees of a wooded mountainside. Through evaporation, the vapour in the atmosphere is replenished, and new clouds are formed. Thus the process is repeated—as the vapour rises and is cooled, it condenses, falls as rain on another mountain, only to evaporate and rise as vapour once again.

Balancing Water in the Air

The water that the hydrologic cycle pumps into the air by evaporation is soon recondensed and distributed as precipitation. At any one time, only about 3,100 cubic miles of water (less than 1/100,000 of the total supply) is held in the atmosphere. Even this fraction, if suddenly released as rain, would be enough to cover the earth with an inch of water.

The hydrologic cycle often short-circuits itself. Much water evaporated from the ocean quickly returns in sea squalls; on land, some rainwater returns to the air as soon as it falls. But the overall amount of water in the air remains constant. Every increment of vapour is ultimately expended, in raindrops, snowflakes or hailstones. Water held in the air is more than potential precipitation. It represents quantities of latent energy, amassed by evaporating molecules. As this energy builds up, the cycle releases it through storms. A run-of-the-mill thunderstorm releases more energy than a 110-kiloton nuclear bomb—and there are more than 10,000 thunderstorms every day.

A Waterlogged Underworld

When rain-water soaks down into the ground, it may not actively return to the hydrologic cycle for decades, centuries or even millennia. The earth holds more than two million cubic miles of water underground—about 37 times the amount stored on the surface in lakes and rivers. About half the ground-water, saturating the soil or seeping through rocky strata at depths down to half a mile, is effectively taking part in the cycle. Usually it does so at a reduced rate, bubbling up in springs—though occasionally the return is sudden, as in steaming fumaroles (*right*) or spewing geysers. The other half, stored between half a mile and three miles down, is unable to return to circulation at all until some interior convulsion of the earth releases it. But no water is permanently shut out of the cycle—not even the stagnated rains of 10,000 years ago, trapped three miles under the earth's crust.

STEAM VENTS IN THE EARTH
Superheated steam forces its way through fissures in the earth's surface, releasing ground-water as vapour. Such spouts, or fumaroles, are formed where an underground oven of hot rock converts water to steam. Steam pressure builds up until it drives the vapour through vents in the earth. Fumaroles, such as these in New Zealand, are often found in areas close to volcanoes.

A WELL WITHOUT A PUMP
Soaked to the skin, a workman struggles to staunch the flow of a newly struck gusher of water stored under pressure. Such naturally pressurized, or artesian, wells may continue to spurt indefinitely, as rain-water seeps downwards to replenish the underground store. More commonly, the well depletes the water supply, lowering the pressure and shutting itself off.

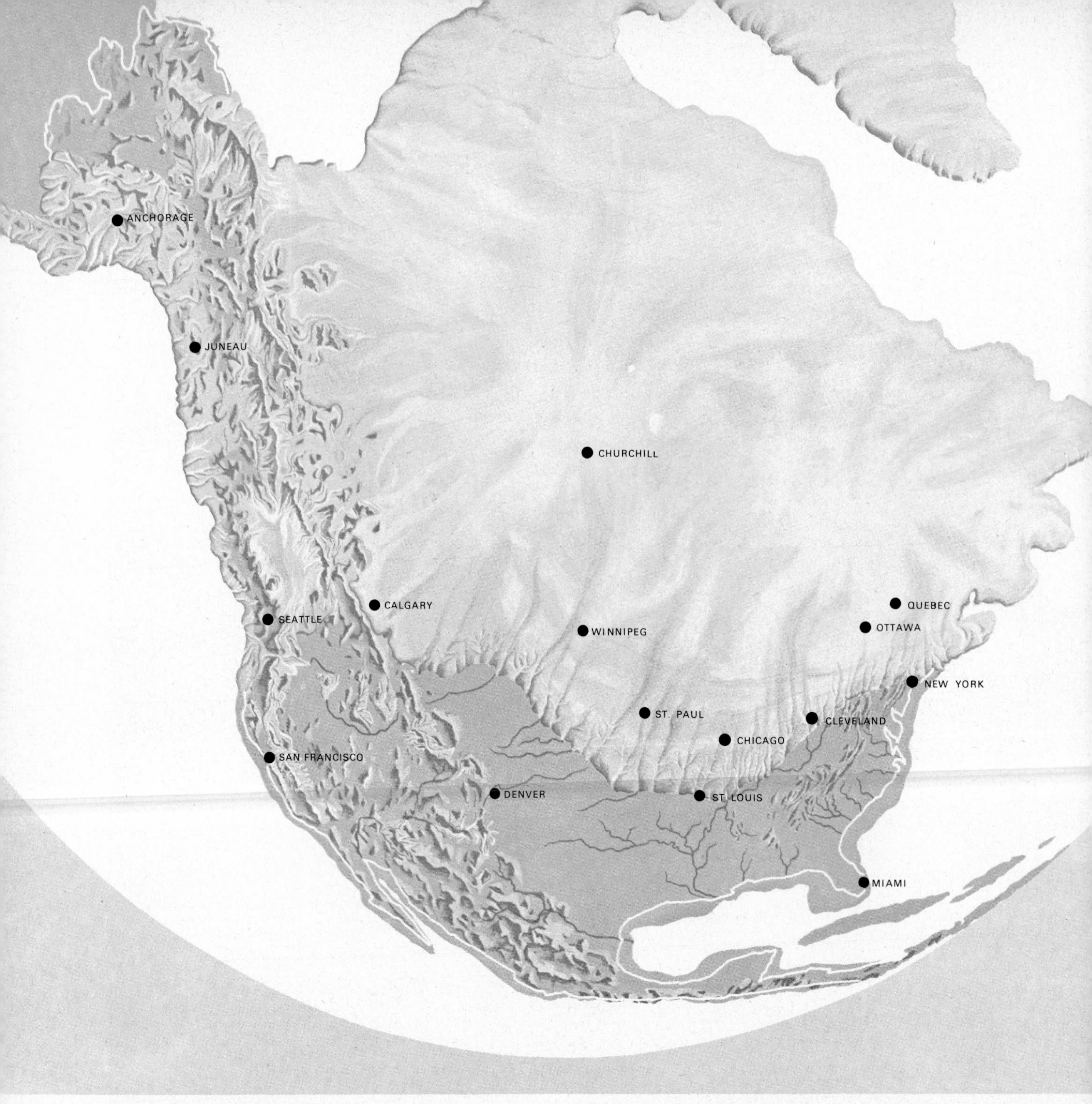

In the ice-age, half of North America was under ice; this composite map shows four waves at once. Present coastlines are outlined.

Aberrations in the Cycle

More than a million years ago the temperature of the earth fell slightly. The total heat loss may have amounted to somewhere about 2° C. But even that small difference in temperature was enough to upset the delicate balance by which the hydrologic cycle had held the earth's climate relatively stable for hundreds of millions of years. With the cycle out of gear, the world entered the Pleistocene era, or ice-age. Scientists believe that it was at least the third time such an event had occurred.

Increasing quantities of the earth's precipitation were stored as ice, and glaciers alternately extended towards the equator and receded. There were four major advances, during which the glaciers wore down the Appala-

Lakes, which covered 20 per cent of North America as the glaciers retreated (*light blue*), cover only 7 per cent today (*dark blue*).

chian Mountains, gouged out the tops of the Alps and the Himalayas, carved out the basins of innumerable lakes, and bulldozed great heaps of earth and rock on every continent. At their greatest extent, the ice sheets, often thousands of feet thick, held more than double the amount of water frozen today. They reached to within 650 miles of the Gulf of Mexico (*above left*).

These changes in the cycle had innumerable side effects. As increasing amounts of the earth's water turned to ice, the ocean levels fell 300 to 400 feet. As a result, about 2.5 million square miles of land were added to eastern North America. Alaska and Asia were connected by a land bridge. The British Isles and Europe were similarly connected. The oceans have since risen close to their former level, engulfing most of the added land again (*above right*).

The glaciers began their fourth retreat only about 10,000 years ago and are still receding. The hydrologic cycle may now have regained its former equilibrium—but there is no way of knowing whether the ice-age is over.

The Transient Lakes

Lakes are anomalies of the hydrologic cycle, short-lived features of the terrain which begin to die the moment they are created. The hottest, driest place in the United States, Death Valley in California, was covered by a lake 180 feet deep only about 20,000 years ago. The Birket Qarûn, a shallow brackish lake in Egypt's Faiyûm province, had once been 15 times its present size. Known during one period as Lake Moeris, it was formed some 70,000 years ago, when the Nile flowed into a low area, and it then held more water than the Nile discharges in a year.

Many lakes die of an excess of sediment. Sand and gravel settle on the bottom, slowly turning the lake into a mud flat or swamp, and finally filling the lake entirely. As some lakes die, new ones replace them. The appearance of lakes is often associated with changes in the hydrologic cycle. Scientists calculate that early in the Pleistocene, the semi-arid New Mexico country was changed into a region dotted with ponds and lakes as the average temperature dropped by 3° C., and the annual rainfall increased by nine inches. When the temperature rose again and precipitation diminished, the lakes dried up.

THE LIFE-SPAN OF A LAKE
The near-freezing water of Lake Schrader in Alaska, fed by melting snow from Mount Chamberlin, causes vapour in the warmer air to condense into morning mist. The lake, one of the northernmost in Alaska, was formed about 13,000 years ago, during the last glacial advance. If it continues to silt up at its present rate, Lake Schrader will be gone 10,000 years from now.

3

The Underground Reservoir

GROUND-WATER RISES TO THE SURFACE OF THE SAHARA AT THE OASIS OF OUNIANGA KEBIR, FORMING SPRINGS WHICH CREATE AN ISLAND OF LUSH GREENERY IN THE DESERT.

EVEN IN THIS AGE OF HOMAGE to rational science, the ancient rites of the water witches survive. Several years ago, a group of dowsers, meeting in the little Vermont town of Danville, demonstrated a search for water. They tramped across several acres of meadow, divining rods extended, until a mysterious tug signified the location of a water "vein". Eight feet down they dug, 10 feet, then 12 feet—the predicted depth. The pit remained as dry as the scorched dust of summer. Sifting the soil through his fingers, one dowser said, "We didn't dig deep enough."

He was absolutely right. In most parts of the world, any hole dug deep enough will yield water—with or without the aid of the diviner's forked hazel stick. Water is plentiful in New England, and at least two to five gallons of water per minute can be produced from almost any hole deeper than 20 feet. Near Miami, a yield of 800 to 1,300 gallons per minute is considered commonplace from wells averaging 50 feet in depth. The sand underlying Tallulah, Louisiana, yields 6,000 gallons per minute. Even around Tucson, drillers count on striking a dependable household supply at several hundred feet.

Potable water exists in the ground—in some quantity, in some form, at some depth—nearly everywhere on earth. The Sahara itself, a synonym for total aridity, is underlain by water: an estimated 150,000 cubic miles spreading over 2.5 million square miles of land area. Indeed, almost all of the world's stock of fresh water—two million cubic miles, or more than 97 per cent of the total available—is inside the earth. Half of this huge supply is believed to be within a half mile of the surface and is therefore reasonably accessible.

Most underground water is constantly in motion, ultimately to emerge at the surface again, pulled by gravity from under sloping terrain into springs and streams, lifted up by plants and pumped out by man. Its vast bulk, travelling out of sight, supplies much of the water used for drinking, washing and industrial processing. Water dissolves salts from the earth; it creates caves and the stalactites and stalagmites that ornament them; it produces bubbling mineral springs and showy geysers.

Since ground-water is hidden, the existence of superstition about its location is almost inevitable, and descriptions of its movement underground are not only capricious but often bizarre. Few untrained men, particularly in humid areas where water is relatively abundant, know much about reading the surface signs of it. In dry areas, however, weather and water supply are subjects of absorbing interest, and many a farmer in Arizona and New Mexico can guess the volume of a stream, the amount of water that a field of grain will require and the possible depth of subsurface water.

Ground-water is no more mysterious in its nature and movement than water on the surface and in the air. Whatever the environment, water exhibits its usual remarkable properties and obeys the general laws of physics and chemistry. Gravity attracts the water from the skies, pulls it beneath the surface of the ground, distributes it among permeable layers and influences the directions in which it will flow.

Wherever precipitation touches the earth, some of it soaks in. It seeps downwards towards the centre of the earth until blocked at some depth by non-porous rock; simultaneously it spreads out horizontally so that vast volumes of earth become saturated with water. The water soaks into the dirt and moves through the permeable earth from pore to pore. Only rarely, in a few caverns, does ground-water exist in clearly defined pools or flow in identifiable streams. There are no "veins" of water. A well is simply a hole reaching down into the saturated region. Water seeps from the saturated earth into the hole and any hole in the neighbourhood, dug to the same depth, will usually produce just as successfully.

A watery underworld

The proportion of water that sinks into the ground varies with the character of the soil. If the soil is dry and porous, large amounts will seep in. The worst condition for absorption is a sudden downpour of rain on a sloping surface of less permeable material, such as clay; most of that precipitation will quickly run off the surface.

The outermost surface of the earth is composed largely of porous, fairly loose material, principally sand, gravel, silt and decayed vegetation. Most of this surface is underlain by porous rock such as sandstone and limestone. Beneath this everywhere is bedrock, so compact, as a result of molten origin or of subsequent heat and pressure, that it is totally impermeable. All layers above this impermeable base rock hold groundwater. The layers are classified by water content into two regions: the zone of aeration and the zone of saturation.

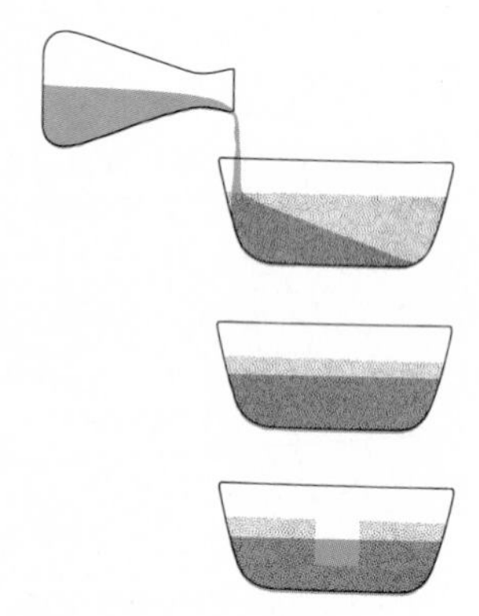

A WATER-TABLE is formed through a process similar to the one shown above: water running into soil (*top*) sinks in and forms an underlying layer of saturated earth (*centre*). A hole dug in the earth—in other words, a well—will fill up to the level of the water-table (*bottom*). The water-table varies in depth according to precipitation: it is closest to the surface in wet periods and farther down during droughts, when wells sometimes go dry.

Seeping below the surface, water first enters the zone of aeration, a transition level where the earth contains both water and air. Its depth varies widely, from an inch or less near the edge of a swamp to hundreds or thousands of feet elsewhere. In this zone, water shows its powers of adhesion by clinging to particles of soil and rock. The amount held in the pore spaces by this molecular attraction fluctuates widely and rapidly. Immediately after a rainstorm, the zone of aeration may be surfeited with water; shortly after, it may contain little; during a prolonged drought, it may contain almost none at all. Some water that enters this region sinks through to the layers beneath; some is absorbed by plants or evaporates into the air. The zone of aeration ends in a moist region called the capillary fringe. It contains water lifted from the still-lower zone of saturation by capillary action. Its depth depends upon the diameter of the soil's pores: if the pores are relatively large, little water will be drawn up and the belt will be narrow; but if they are fine-bored and continuous, water may climb as high as eight feet. Sometimes, though not often, this "fringe" reaches all the way to the surface.

The lower moist layer, comprising the zone of saturated earth, forms a principal water resource. Wells dip into it; springs, rivers and lakes are its natural outcroppings on the surface of the globe. Water seeping downwards can go no farther; every pore, crack and interstice is filled.

The top of the saturation zone—the boundary between it and the capillary fringe—is called the ground-water table, or simply the water-table. The water glinting at the bottom of a shallow well is an exposed part of the water-table. Around it and continuous with it, the same water-table extends—whether exposed or not, above the ground or in it. The surfaces of lakes and rivers are also exposures of the water-table and, to an hydrologist's eye, blend with the water-table into the landscape.

This relationship of earth to water-table can be demonstrated by pouring water into a sand-filled tub. The water sinks through the sand and disappears, and soon the surface is completely dry. If holes are poked deep into the sand to simulate wells, and if grooves and pockets are scooped out to simulate river channels and lake basins, the water will appear at the bottom of each depression, and will reach precisely the same level in each. That level is the water-table of the sand tub.

The tub of sand is an oversimplified model of an aquifer—a layer of gravel, sand, porous rock or other coarse materials through which water flows more freely than elsewhere in the earth. Few aquifers are as homogeneous as the sand in the tub; their contained water meets differing degrees of flow resistance, due to differences in porosity and particle size. As a result, the water flows at varying speeds in seeking its level, and it almost never becomes truly level, as it does in the sand-tub model.

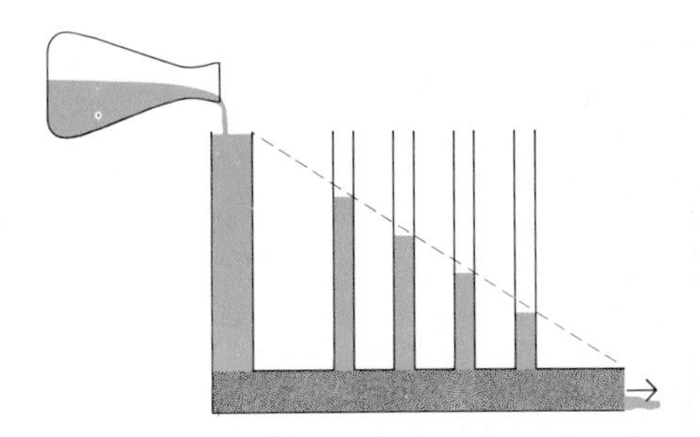

DECLINING PRESSURES that occur in artesian water systems are explained by this diagram. Artesian water, trapped deep in the ground, is under great pressure near its source. When tapped by a well in this area, it surges up strongly. As it flows underground, artesian water encounters friction, which reduces its head of pressure. As wells are drilled farther from the source, the water in them rises to lower and lower levels.

The rise and fall of water-tables

The changing elevations in the earth's water-table are revealed by its surface waters. Some lakes are higher than others. Streams run downhill. The water-table, which must connect them all, also slopes. Its contours reflect in part the landscape above it; it is high under mountains and dips towards river valleys. Occasionally, the surface contour drops more sharply than the water-table beneath it. It cuts into the water-table and exposes saturated earth so that water issues forth: a spring. If a wide swath of the land's surface dips beneath the water-table, a lake or swamp occurs. Across the lowest dip of a valley the water-table supplies a river. In fact, a river's channel is often a continuous spring that sustains the river's flow under sunny skies when no rain falls.

One of the factors influencing the contour of the water-table is the contour of the land above it. This connection is best seen in an idealized landscape: a low and gently sloping hill with a river valley on either side, all underlain by homogeneous porous material. As rain falls and seeps downwards, water accumulates underground at the base of the porous material. The water-table rises uniformly, as in the sand-tub model. It remains essentially flat until, as more rain falls, it rises so far above the base that it reaches the lowest portions of the two valleys. It will now seep out into the valleys and fill those channels.

Thereafter, ground-water feeds into the two rivers. As rain continues to fall on the hills, it soaks into the earth, seeps down to the aquifer and—since the aquifer is now higher than the valley—seeps out of the sides of the hill. If the amount seeping out of the hill and drained off by the river channels precisely equalled the amount soaking into the ground to add to the aquifer, the water-table would not change. But friction intervenes. Friction occurs between the water and the walls of the interstices through which it moves; to a lesser degree, friction also occurs between sliding planes of molecules within the liquid itself. The water, its movement thus retarded, piles up under the hill.

Now the water-table is no longer level, but peaked. Its highest point lies immediately below the hill-top, its lowest near the river surfaces. The table's steepest slopes resemble the slopes of the hill but are considerably less abrupt.

Nature's complex plumbing

The elevation of parts of the water-table causes water to move underground. The water above presses down on the water beneath, just as it does in the pipes in a house. For the underground water system operates like a vast natural plumbing system. The flow of water through its pores and spaces is governed by the same factors that govern the flow of water through man-made piping: the size of the pipes and the pressure pushing water through.

The water-transporting pores in the ground connect to form extended passage-ways. If the pores are large, water meets little resistance and easily flows through. If they are small, or if the passage-way has to carry water over a long distance, the flow is retarded. The flow halts completely against non-porous material.

Unlike a municipal water installation, nature's underground plumbing system cannot maintain an even flow. A change in any of the physical factors described above may reduce or increase the flow of groundwater. The flow increases when water from rain or snow percolates down faster than it flows out at the point of discharge; the water-table elevates, raising the pressure head. Conversely, the flow abates when incoming water does not equal the outflow, lowering the water-table and the pressure head. Should the water rise at the discharge point, the pressure head again lessens; as the height difference between source and discharge point is reduced, discharge and flow decline. They may halt altogether or even reverse. For example, sudden floods can boost the height of a stream's surface above the water-table. In such a case, water no longer runs from the aquifer into the stream; the flow reverses and water runs out of the stream into the river banks.

The pressure moving underground water often is not great. Water seeps into wells and trickles from springs. But occasionally a hole in the ground taps water under great pressure. This condition, common to many regions, is called artesian. The name comes from the province of Artois in northern France, where a series of productive wells stirred interest in the 12th century, but artesian conditions have been recognized for thousands of years. Many centuries before Christ, the Chinese brought in artesian wells by driving bamboo casings down many hundreds of feet; the job often required generations to complete, and the wells were called "grandfather wells".

The pressure that powers artesian wells is created when ground-water seeps between two layers of non-permeable materials. These layers prevent the release of water. They act like the walls of a pipe, and can hold water under pressure. The pressure is generated as the aquifer slopes down through the earth, the water at upper levels pressing on confined water lower down. The amount of pressure released where a well pierces the wall depends on the difference in elevation between that point and the highest level of water in the aquifer. This difference may be great, since water may fill an artesian aquifer nearly to the top of the "pipe".

Artesian aquifers can be found at any depth, but many plunge far into the earth. In London, wells were dug in the 18th and 19th centuries to a depth of 300 to 500 feet into the water-saturated chalk layer, sandwiched between clay strata, underlying a large area beneath the city. They continue to supply millions of gallons daily.

Not until the mid-19th century was artesian water reached by drilling with efficient cable tools. One of the first such wells was completed in the Paris suburb of Grenelle in 1841. It took seven years to drill, aroused international interest, reached a depth of 1,798 feet and, when it came in, stunned the drilling crew by shooting a parabolic fountain high in the air. In near-by Passy, soon after, a well was sunk 1,900 feet into the same saturated substratum. From the completed bore-hole a continuous stream of water spurted 54 feet above ground at a rate of more than five million gallons a day.

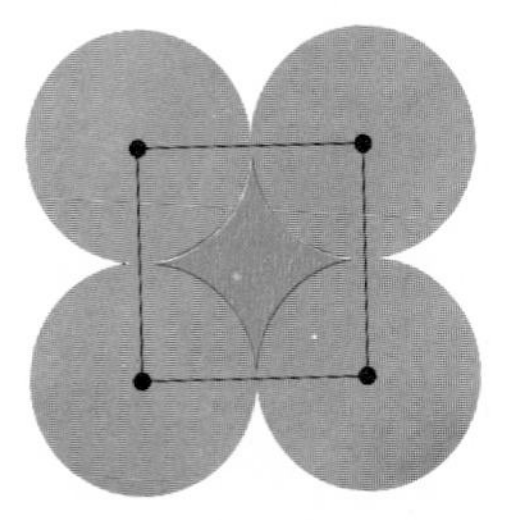

THE POROSITY OF SOIL, which strongly affects the availability of ground-water, may vary greatly in equal quantities of matter. In the two examples shown here, for example, the amount of substance is the same in each case, but one is almost twice as porous as the other. The rock above (perhaps sandstone) is 47.6 per cent porous; by contrast, the porosity of the soil below (which might be clay) is only 25.9 per cent.

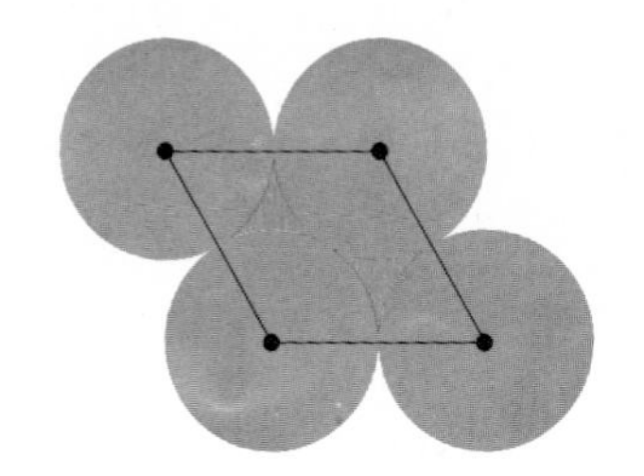

A hot-water system

The same type of geological formation that supplies cold water from artesian wells is also the source of many hot, or thermal, springs. Artesian aquifers often dip deep into the earth, and the underground temperature increases with depth—about 1°C. for every 100 feet. If the impermeable rock layers confining the water dip down far enough, they may carry it to regions that will heat it to high temperatures.

One of the better-known thermal springs is that at Warm Springs, Georgia, where President Roosevelt and many other polio patients were treated. The source of its water is rain falling on Pine Mountain, two miles south of the village. The rain sifts into a permeable rock formation known locally as the Hollis, which carries it northwards for a mile at a depth of a few hundred feet. Its average temperature at the start is about 17°C. The Hollis plunges down to 3,000 feet, where it ends against impermeable rock. The water, now hot and also under pressure, is turned back. Forced to the top, it emerges at a temperature of 31°C.

Man-made connections to the underground plumbing system influence its operation, sometimes drastically. Withdrawing water from an aquifer at any one place inevitably affects the entire aquifer. This is true of artesian systems as well as water-table aquifers. Withdrawal may decrease the flow, the pressure, the amount delivered, or all three. Unless the recharge of the aquifer equals the rate of withdrawal, the supply will ultimately dwindle.

Even a single well has pronounced effects on the water-table. The well takes water from the saturated earth around it, literally drying out part of the saturated zone and causing a dent to form in the water-table's smooth surface. When heavy pumping removes water from the well more rapidly than the inflow replaces it, the dent in the water-table becomes an increasingly deep, wide cone. It becomes what hydrologists term a "cone of depression"—a conical section of the water table depleted of water. Cones of depression form around every well from which water is drawn. Each depression cone, by increasing the pressure head locally, boosts the flow from the surrounding area of an aquifer until the inflow to the well balances the rate of withdrawal. Artesian water also must be replenished if the flow is to be maintained. Discharge from the wells must be matched gallon for gallon by recharge into the aquifer over a period of time. This balance rarely occurs, and many wells that once flowed under their own pressure now require pumping.

In the mid-western United States, a classic example of artesian condition occurs in a great sandstone layer, sandwiched between two impermeable rock layers, which comes to the surface in the Black Hills of Wyoming and South Dakota. The aquifer receives rain and surface run-off and transports the water underground, curving across several States. Many richly flowing wells owe their productivity to this great aquifer. But since the 1890s, while demands on the Black Hills supply have multiplied, the pressure and rate of flow of these artesian wells have declined greatly. The level in a well near Pierre on the river Missouri dropped 300 feet in 35 years.

The waters of antiquity

The continuing drain on water supplies already tapped has prompted suggestions for probing deeper into the earth's stock of underground water. There are many water-bearing layers below even those now tapped by artesian wells and they contain far more water than the sources now being used.

Some of this untouched water has been trapped deep in the earth for millions of years, buried in the pores of sedimentary rock laid down beneath ancient seas. It is called connate water, from a Latin word meaning "born at the same time". Connate water has been absent from the hydrological cycle for ages. But there is also water inside the earth that has never taken part in the hydrologic cycle. It is part of the original supply of water molecules that were drawn from cosmic dust to form the earth thousands of millions of years ago. It may exist as steam or it may be bound into crystalline rocks as water of hydration. Occasionally some of this "juvenile" water escapes to the surface by volcanic action.

Unfortunately, neither connate nor juvenile water is usable for most purposes. It has been held deep in the earth, where it is hot and under great pressure. In intimate contact with mineral substances for many hundreds of millions of years, this hot, pressurized water has become loaded with dissolved salts.

Tapping deep sources of the earth's water is not only impractical, it also seems unnecessary. The supplies of fresh ground-water fairly close to the surface are more than ample to fill human needs if all of them are explored and properly managed. And growing understanding of the nature of water underground is making the search for usable water less a matter of art and luck, and more a reliable, scientific procedure.

Nature teamed with technology

Simple facts have long served to guide the seeker after a water supply. Since the water-table—the upper boundary of available water—slopes less steeply than the ground, it is closer to the earth's surface at the bottom of a hill. Such a location has been favoured by well-diggers for thousands of years. Surface water, in ponds, swamps, streams, offers an even stronger hint; there the water-table has actually emerged from below ground. The flora of an area provides another of nature's simple clues, for plants indicate the presence of water as well as its absence. In arid lands, the xerophytes—literally, "dry plants"—attest to water's scarcity. Cactus, for example, adapts to the lack of water and its presence denotes the absence of readily accessible water. The phreatophytes, or "well plants", on the other hand, grow only where they can send roots deep into the capillary fringe and, indeed, into the water-table itself. To the trained observer, they say, "Dig here". Several phreatophytes—salt grass, mesquite and greasewood—betoken the presence of water in some arid regions; in other areas the willow tree, sycamore, cottonwood and palm tree are equally important indicators.

While nature's hints are helpful, the finding of water rests heavily today on growing technology. The supply for a modern town is so important that careful—and expensive—investigation is warranted. Studies of the geology of an area and of its existing wells enable an engineer to eliminate large areas as unproductive and choose the most favourable zones for the occurrence of water. He may drill test holes to reveal what lies beneath, or he may turn to indirect methods. Two commonly used techniques depend on electrical resistivity and seismic refraction. The former measures the amount of resistance offered to an electrical current by underground rock structures. The seismic-refraction method measures the speed with which a surface shock—usually from a dynamite explosion—travels a known distance through the earth. The velocity of the shock wave tells whether rock structures several hundred feet under the surface are porous or solid and, if porous, whether they hold water. Water content increases the velocity of the shock wave; porosity decreases it.

Aerial photographs of an area are also one of hydrology's valuable tools. A trained hydrologist will read from them marks of erosion, vegetation, drainage patterns, gravel pits and other significant signs of ground-water. And more elaborate research on a broad scale—including analyses of ground-water movements over large areas with the aid of an electronic computer—is providing the basic knowledge that will solve the remaining mysteries of water-seeking.

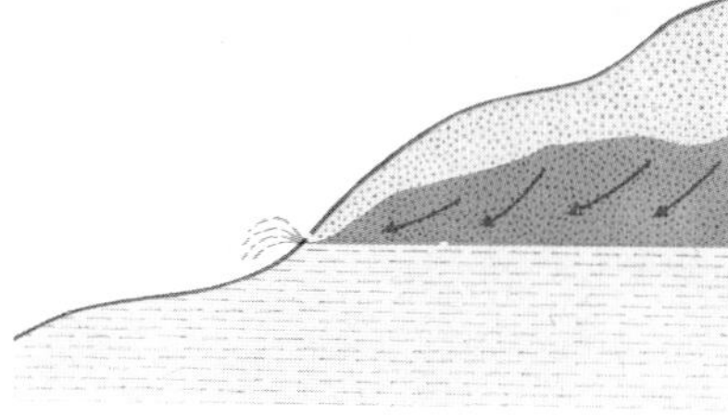

WATER-TABLE

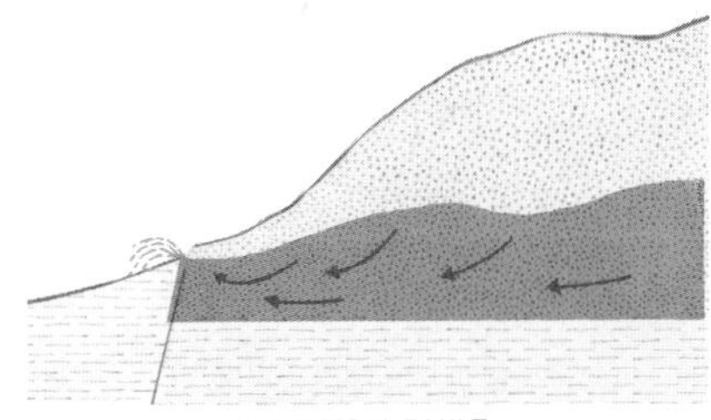

GEOLOGICAL FAULT

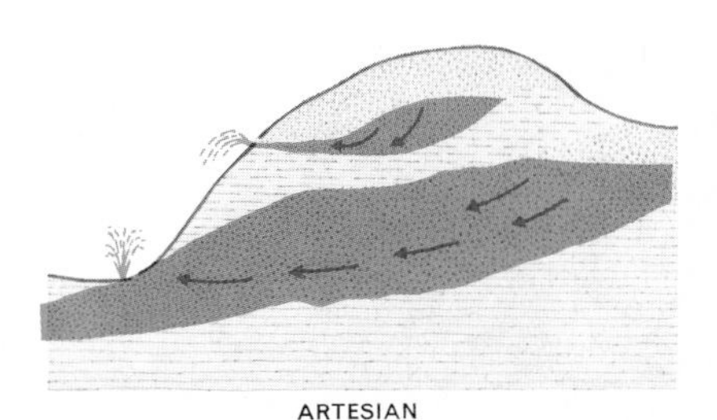

ARTESIAN

A SPRING IS BORN usually in one of three ways. Most often ground-water filling all available pore space above a layer of rock simply surfaces as a spring (*top*). Sometimes a layer of ground-water is exposed by a geological fault created when a shift occurs in the earth's strata (*centre*). The third type of spring is found where a layer of artesian water, usually under great pressure, broaches the surface (shown at the bottom, with a common water-table spring above it for comparison).

Mapping a World of Ground-Water

Spreading everywhere under the earth's surface, ground-water constitutes a major source of usable water. It fills the wells of towns and farms, and helps to replenish the supplies of large cities. Where surface water is scarce, ground-water is so vital for irrigation that men have fought over the right to tap it. It is distributed everywhere about the earth—under the arid flats of Death Valley in the United States and the highest peaks of the Himalayas alike. It slowly seeps through surface soil or settles in deeply buried strata, where it is trapped at great pressures. Only half a mile down, there are an estimated 50,000 cubic miles of water beneath the United States alone.

To map, manage and conserve this resource, hundreds of scientists are engaged in tracing its vague wanderings. They perform a miracle of detection: although they rarely see the ground-water—except when it seeps into a well—they can estimate how much is stored under any county across the continent, how fast it is moving, how soon pumping of one well will affect another's yield, where water under a farm came from and where it will be decades in the future.

CARVER OF EERIE CAVERNS
Lying 200 feet below the surface, an enormous blue-lit cavern, laced with calcite, stretches for miles beneath the Ozark National Forest in the United States. Caves like these, assumed by many people to be a major source of ground-water, are actually quite rare. The pools or rivers in these cavernous formations represent only 5 per cent of the total ground-water reserves of the earth.

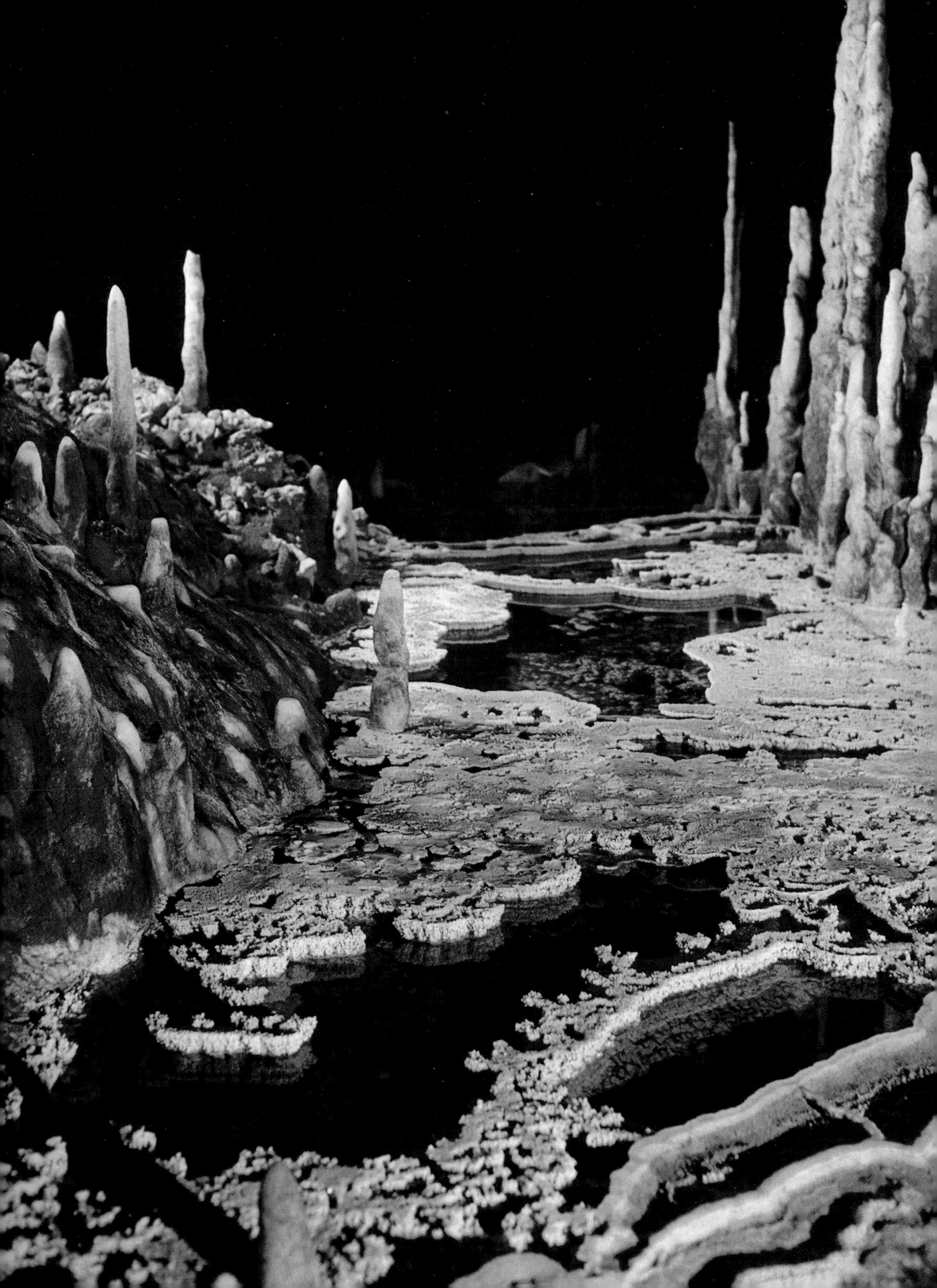

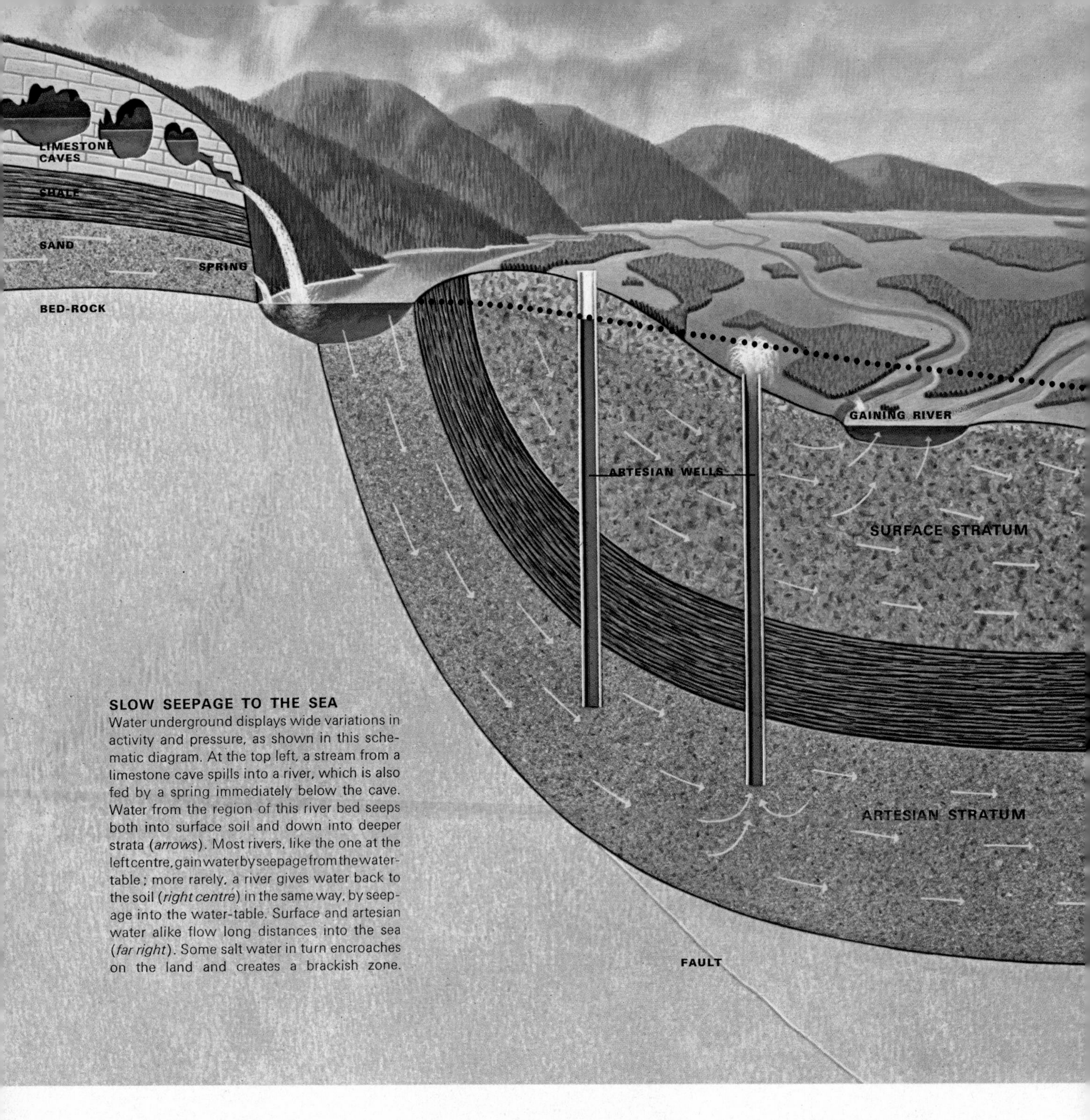

SLOW SEEPAGE TO THE SEA
Water underground displays wide variations in activity and pressure, as shown in this schematic diagram. At the top left, a stream from a limestone cave spills into a river, which is also fed by a spring immediately below the cave. Water from the region of this river bed seeps both into surface soil and down into deeper strata (*arrows*). Most rivers, like the one at the left centre, gain water by seepage from the water-table; more rarely, a river gives water back to the soil (*right centre*) in the same way, by seepage into the water-table. Surface and artesian water alike flow long distances into the sea (*far right*). Some salt water in turn encroaches on the land and creates a brackish zone.

A Ponderous Underground Flow

Falling as rain or flowing in rivers, water seeps into the soil and begins a massive underground migration. Ground-water roves as restlessly as any river, although its movement is often extremely slow. It might take 135 years for water to travel laterally through a single mile of sand.

A considerable quantity of ground-water soaks the soil near the surface. Bounded at the bottom by a rocky barrier, water seeps downwards until it creates a zone of total saturation. The top of this zone is known as the water-table. Not all water remains near the surface, however. Impelled by gravity, some ground-water finds its way into deeper artesian strata, where it is caught between impermeable layers of rock and held under pressure by the weight of the water above. It often spreads over 20-mile stretches and runs out into distant surface soil or into the sea. The height to which this pressurized water will rise if tapped (indicated

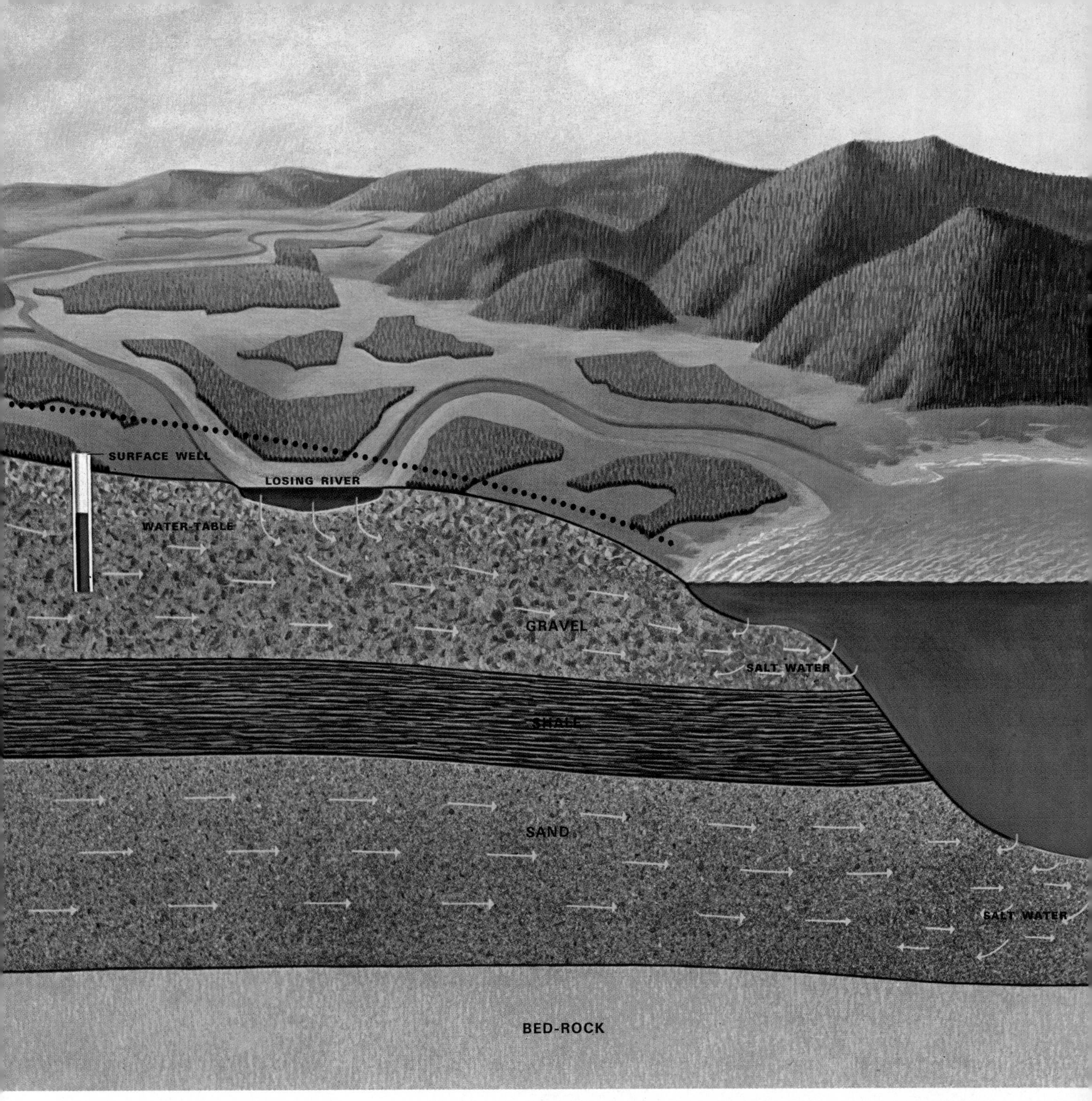

by the dotted line above) diminishes as the water flows farther from its source.

To tap ground-water, a well can be dug into the surface soil, or drilled deeper down to an artesian stratum. A surface well, dipping into the water-table, simply fills up like a straw stuck into a glass. But an artesian well taps water under pressure; it comes surging upwards, often higher than the water-table and sometimes many feet higher than the land itself.

GRAVEL SHALE SAND

WATER-TABLE

CHANNELS AND BARRIERS
Shale, sand and gravel all store water, but they transmit it at varying speeds. Water passes easily through the large and loosely packed grains of gravel. It travels more slowly through sand, which has small pores, and scarcely at all through shale, whose pores are not interconnected.

A Vigil over Dwindling Reserves

Indiscriminate tapping of ground-water has brought farmers to the brink of disaster in some parts of the country. When too much water was drawn from a stratum under California's San Joaquin Valley, the land, rent by deep fissures, sank as much as 23 feet. Overdraft of ground-water in one part of Arizona lowered the water-table by 400 feet—and 320,000 acres of farmland were lost as the cost of irrigation became prohibitive.

The threat of such catastrophes keeps hundreds of hydrologists out in the field checking wells and testing artesian pressures. For almost two-thirds of all wells in the U.S., "biography" cards (with data on the amount of water pumped and the type of soil tapped) are on file with the U.S. Geological Survey. This government agency, with accountants' caution, keeps track of the ground-water reserves of the entire nation.

A TELLTALE PRESSURE TEST
On a capped artesian well near Phoenix, an hydrologist reads a meter which shows changes of water pressure in a buried stratum. Some instruments used to determine well pressure are so sensitive to underground fluctuations that they also pick up shock waves of earthquakes and underground nuclear explosions —and can even distinguish between the two.

A YARDSTICK FOR IRRIGATION
Above a small dam that backs up well water pumped for a California irrigation project, a gauge records on a drum how much water is flowing into the ditches. Knowing the flow, and estimating how much water will evaporate or be used by plants, engineers calculate how much will return to the ground. Thus they can foretell changes in the level of the water-table.

TAKING THE PULSE OF A WELL

With stop-watch and flow-meter, a field-worker measures the pumping rate of a well every half hour. He also checks how far the water-table drops. Combining these figures, experts calculate the yield of the well. Whenever feasible, a new well is given this pump test. Data from all tests in a region, fed into a computer, enable scientists to map future water-table contours.

As one U.S.G.S. scientist (*standing*) connects a voltmeter to the ground-water computer for Kansas and Nebraska, another (*right*) reads on an

Computing an End to Water Wars

On the 27th May, 1927, a band of California farmers dynamited an aqueduct carrying water to a near-by county. Other "water wars" have been fought with pitchforks, shotguns and fists. Recently, such a dispute arose between Kansas and Nebraska—and was analysed by the analogue computer above. It was feared that the wells for a proposed Nebraska irrigation project would lower the water-table and impair the flow of a river that supplied Kansas farms. The U.S.G.S. was able to indicate sites

oscilloscope how far the water-table will fall in 50 years. From such spot readings, the scientist on the left is drawing a water-table contour map

for the irrigation-project wells, and also reassure the Kansas farmers that their river would not run dry.

The brain behind this hydrological soothsaying is a giant circuit that electrically simulates the actual soil conditions, the water usage, the directions of flow and the water-table level in any ground-water system. The computer can accurately predict what changes will occur in water-table contours in any part of the region, depending on how much water is drawn out over a given period of time. The components of this computer (described in detail on the next two pages) made it possible to reduce the contested area of Kansas and Nebraska, a ground-water system covering 7,600 square miles, to a manageable 53 square feet of electric circuit.

A scientist works on the computer for a ground-water system. Its construction required 30,400 resistors. An average TV set has about 125.

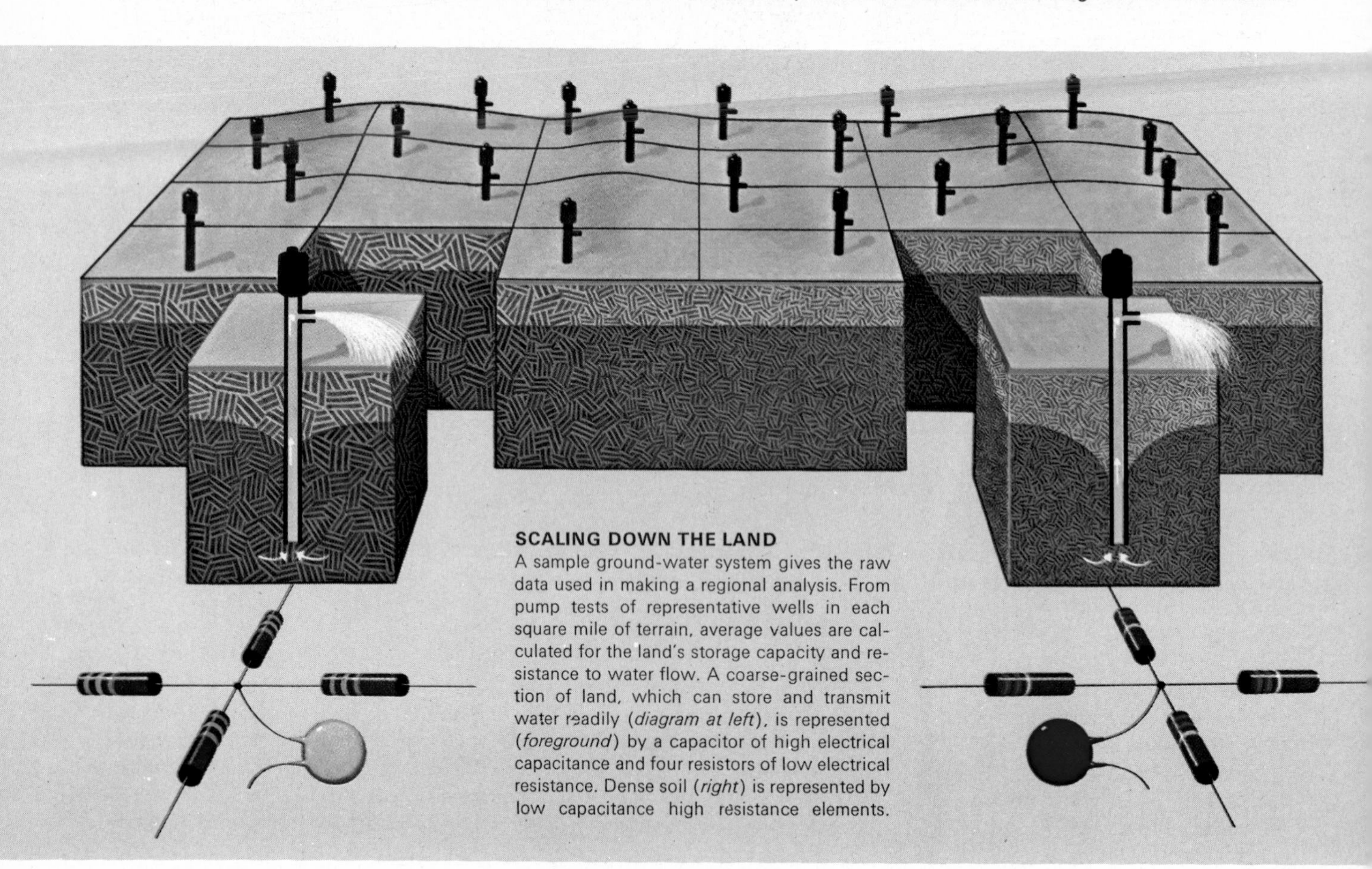

SCALING DOWN THE LAND

A sample ground-water system gives the raw data used in making a regional analysis. From pump tests of representative wells in each square mile of terrain, average values are calculated for the land's storage capacity and resistance to water flow. A coarse-grained section of land, which can store and transmit water readily (*diagram at left*), is represented (*foreground*) by a capacitor of high electrical capacitance and four resistors of low electrical resistance. Dense soil (*right*) is represented by low capacitance high resistance elements.

A Circuit to Simulate Flow

The computer that weighed facts in the water dispute between Kansas and Nebraska took a month to build. It uses electricity to imitate the storage and flow of water in soil, through the use of resistors and capacitors: a resistor impedes current much as soil impedes the flow of water; a capacitor stores electricity much as soil stores water.

After gathering data on the actual terrain, scientists simulate soil characteristics they have measured for each square mile by combining a capacitor and four resistors that are appropriate to that square mile. If the soil is easily permeated by water, the resistors chosen have low resistance to electricity. If the soil can store large quantities of water, a capacitor is used that has a high rating for electrical capacitance—i.e., that stores a large quantity of electricity. Thus, the flow of current through the circuit corresponds with considerable accuracy to the flow of water through the actual terrain.

The water-table level at any geographical spot can be determined by simply measuring the voltage at the corresponding spot on the computer. The circuit is checked out by simulating an actual pumping period, and then comparing the results with farmers' records for the same period. To study the effects of a still-unbuilt irrigation project, experimenters draw more electricity from the appropriate site on the model. The future drop in the water-table will be indicated by a voltage drop in the circuit. Thus, water-table contours can be mapped decades ahead. This is routine work for the computer, which can "pump" a century's worth of "water" in a few millionths of a second.

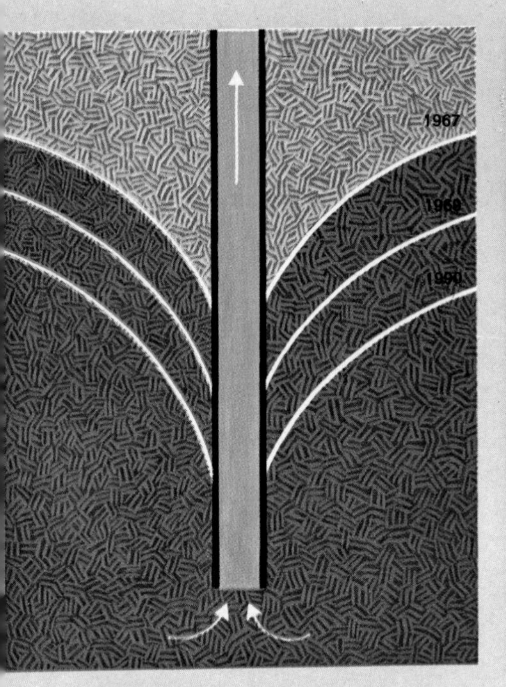

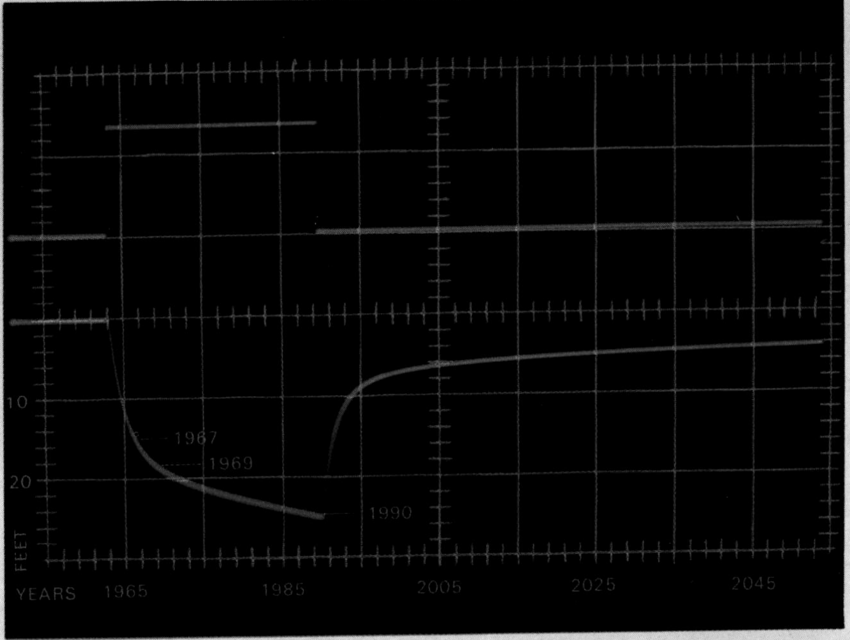

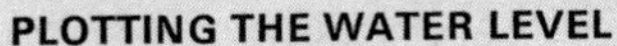
PLOTTING THE WATER LEVEL

The drop in a water-table where a well is in use, shown schematically above (*left*) can be predicted on an electronic graph, as shown on the right. This graph is produced by an oscilloscope that is connected to a simulated ground-water circuit. The break in the upper bar indicates when a well pump, which delivers four gallons per minute, is turned on and off. The lower bar, representing the change in water level, shows a steep drop when the pump is turned on and a steep rise when it is turned off. Afterwards the water level gradually rises.

Searching Out Agents of Waste

Scientists, constantly confronted by unusual ground-water problems, must often use great ingenuity to study them. The salt cedar tree, common in the south-western United States, has posed one such problem. Extending its roots down to the water-table, this tree breathes ground-water into the air through its leaves, causing a loss of 20 million million gallons to the atmosphere each year over 900,000 square miles of the western U.S. Hydrologists have studied the salt cedar's wasteful habits by flying moisture-sensitive instruments over the trees and radioing data back to a computer on the ground. Large-scale attempts have been made to uproot and poison these trees, but so far they have proved too hardy to eradicate.

Ground-water is lost in countless other ways, including contamination. Today scientists are studying such problems as seepage of acid out of mine shafts; pollution of rain over urban areas; and contamination of soil by detergents used in urban areas.

A STAND OF PROFLIGATE TREES
Perched on a hill-top high above a field of salt cedar trees in Arizona (*above left*), a van serves as headquarters for hydrologists conducting research on these water-wasting trees. The van, also shown below, houses a computer used to analyse data radioed back from a special research plane. On top of the van is a radar antenna, used to track the path of the plane.

MARKING MOISTURE FROM THE AIR
Collecting data, a scientist talks by radio to the pilot of a research plane (*background*), heading towards salt cedar trees. Flying to and fro at low altitude over the field, experts record increased air moisture on specially sensitive infra-red film. From data on the air's moisture, temperature and pressure, a computer can calculate how much water the trees waste.

4

Sculpturing the Planet

HIMALAYAN RIVER CARVES TWIN PATHWAY THROUGH SHELF OF SOLID ROCK ON ITS WAY TO THE BAY OF BENGAL.

On a hot September day in 1540, García López de Cárdenas, scouting what is now northern Arizona for the great Spanish explorer Coronado, crossed a level plateau that seemed to stretch unbroken for mile upon mile. Suddenly, with no warning, he found himself at the brink of an abyss—an astounding gash in the surface of the earth, in places a mile in depth, but so abrupt that it could not be seen by a man standing more than a few feet from its edge. Cárdenas was the first European to look into the Grand Canyon. But its desolate grandeur—the great steep cliffs gaudily banded like a many-coloured sandwich cake—has since dazzled thousands upon thousands of observers. It is perhaps the most spectacular sight among the world's landscapes. At the very bottom, hidden from the rim, flows the river Colorado, as muddy as is implied by its name, which is the Spanish word for "red". It was the river that made the gorge, slowly grinding, a fraction of an inch at a time, through the red and buff sandstone, green shale and grey and red limestone, until at last it had gouged its present channel into the tough, thousand-million-year-old black gneiss at the bottom.

Water shaped not only this grandiose landscape but, in one way or another, all the world's landscapes. The gross features of the earth—the ocean basins, continental masses, mountain ranges—were established by movements of the earth's crust. But the fine details—the contours of hill and valley, the spreads of plain—are entirely owing to the action of water, with some assistance from wind. Everywhere on this globe is evident the work of water.

All the physical and chemical properties of water aided in this task of transformation. Solid water in the great ice sheets planed and furrowed much of North America and Europe into their characteristic rolling hills dotted with lakes. Glaciers honed the sharp faces of high mountains such as the Matterhorn. The expansion of ice, freezing in crevices and pores, shattered big rocks into little ones. Liquid water dissolved eerie caverns and freakish valleys out of the solid earth. Water-lubricated particles of soil slid slowly down over one another in the "creep" that helps to round the tops of hills. Water in the form of ocean waves broke off shorelines, created and destroyed beaches, crushed rock into sand.

But it is river water, tumbling turbulently here, flowing gently there, that has been the foremost sculptor of landscape. It has achieved this role chiefly by pulling weathered solids from one place to deposit them in another. In the process it has created upstream valleys that, depending on the surrounding earth, are narrow or broad, straight or winding. Downstream the silt suspended in the river acts as an abrasive, grinding watercourses into gorges. Where the silt settles, the river spreads its burden more widely, generating broad valleys, flood-plains and, at the river mouth, often a delta. The majestic scale of this movement of earth is illustrated by the delta of the Tigris and Euphrates, which in 4,500 years has shifted the shore of the Persian Gulf about 180 miles.

All these processes continue now as they have since the hydrologic cycle began. Rainfall and glacier ice, flowing inexorably towards the sea, drag along the land, bit by bit. The high points are steadily levelled down, old hollows filled in, new ones created. If the levelling-down were to continue without interruption, water would eventually smooth the crust of the earth into a round ball entirely covered by ocean. Interruptions, however, always come. Periodically the crust readjusts, raising new mountains and dropping new lowlands. Less often, the climate changes. Either event causes a drastic shift in the distribution of the earth's water and starts the cycle of landscape-sculpturing anew.

A chamois hunter's theory

The process begins with ice. The idea that ice helps to create the landscape is only about 150 years old. One of the first men to suggest it was an untutored guide in the canton of Valais, Switzerland, J. P. Perraudin. He is described merely as "a skilled hunter of chamois, and an amateur in these types of observations", but he studied the spectacular scenery about him with a discerning eye. He noted, high up on the sides of the local valleys, distinctive piles of boulders—rounded, of all sizes and quite unlike the adjacent mountain rocks. These, he reasoned, must have been brought there and left by glaciers that had retreated.

Perraudin's idea won some converts among the Swiss geologists, but encountered even more sceptics, the most important being the brilliant young naturalist at the University in Neuchâtel, Jean Louis Rodolphe Agassiz. Setting out to prove that glaciers could not have moved as far as Perraudin suggested, Agassiz measured over a period of time the location of marker stakes in a mountain glacier—only to discover that the guide was right. This discovery prompted Agassiz to fit together the observations and ideas of many other men into a unified theory; the result was his great concept of climatic change and the ice-age, which he popularized first in Europe and later, during a long and colourful career at Harvard, in the United States.

Geologists are now convinced that several times during the history of the earth its generally mild and equable climate has been interrupted by glacial epochs. During these times immense sheets of ice repeatedly advanced and retreated. Even a small decrease in the average summer temperature—a drop of as little as 2 or 6° C.—would prevent winter snow from melting over broad areas of the earth, there to mass into thick ice sheets. The evidence can be seen in the ground: gravel made up of rocks that otherwise occur only in far-distant places, as well as deposits of unstratified rocks, sand and clay, which must have been pushed into their present positions not by water but by ice.

What causes the climate to change is a matter of argument. The heat received from the sun could diminish for any of several reasons—a wobble in the axis of the earth, thinning of the atmosphere's heat-trapping carbon dioxide, or a variation in the sun's output of energy. Once the ice begins to accumulate, of course, its very presence serves to perpetuate the cold.

Precisely when the Pleistocene ice epoch began we do not know as yet.

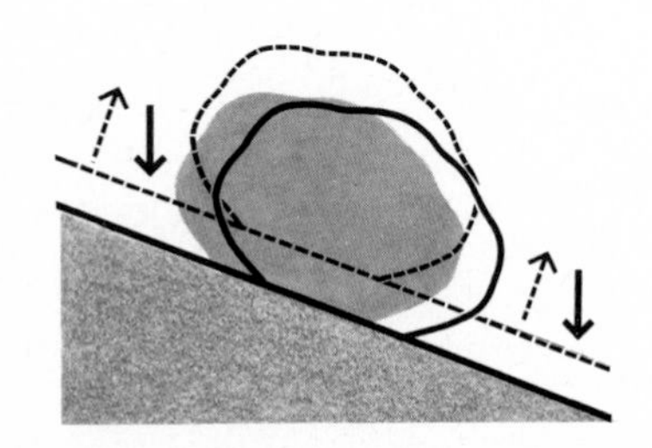

GEOLOGIC "CREEP" occurs when boulders are moved downhill by natural processes, such as the alternate freezing and thawing of ground (*above*). The original position of the boulder above is shown in blue. When water in the topsoil freezes it expands, raising the surface and everything on it, including the boulder (*dotted outline*). At the spring thaw the ground melts, lowering the rock. But instead of returning to the same spot, the boulder slides downhill to a new position (*solid outline*).

Some evidence suggests that the first ice sheets began to move 1.5 million years ago. Other evidence indicates that it began at an even earlier time. Whenever the ice-age began, it was marked by recurrent advances and retreats of the glaciers. At least four major stages—and possibly more—have occurred. These times of glaciers were separated by longer periods of mild climate, with weather probably milder than that which we enjoy today.

The most recent ice-age reached its climax some 50,000 years ago. It covered much of northern Europe, all of Canada, and much of the northern half of the United States with packs often a mile and more thick. In areas now lush and green, the landscape then was a bleak abstraction of white on white, flat and colourless save where some mountain peaks rose up as barren islands above the frozen waste. The world map, too, was far different from that of today. Millions of cubic miles of formerly liquid water, withdrawn from the oceans, was frozen into stupendous ice masses, lowering the general sea level between 300 and 400 ft. It did not leave northern Europe and the U.S. until about 10,000 years ago.

The ice sheets originated in the north and shaped the face of the land by flowing over it, like a solid flood. When they retreated, they did not flow back, but simply melted back from their southern edges, gradually dropping material that they had picked up or swept ahead of them. Stones and pebbles from Scandinavia have been found in Britain, Germany, Poland and some 800 miles away in the Soviet Union.

Glaciers flow downhill, like rivers. They also flow outwards, just as honey dripping on the centre of a table flows outwards from the pressure of the "pile" at the centre. Exactly how this movement is accomplished, however, is still debated. To some extent glaciers slide bodily across the ground, but they also ooze forward like toothpaste squeezed out of a tube, perhaps as layers of the flat ice crystals slide over one another.

The power of a glacier

This ponderous tide picks up rock and sand in several ways as it grinds along. Some is embedded within the ice sheet by an alternation of melting and freezing. The pressures at the bottom of a great mass of ice, particularly when it is being shoved against an unyielding piece of rock, can be enormous—enough to break down the hydrogen bonds in individual ice crystals and turn them into liquid water. This water may trickle down around the rock and, as the pressure eases, refreeze. This alternate thawing and freezing due to changes in pressure can gradually work rocks of considerable size up into the ice sheet, which takes them along with it on its slow travels. Melted water can also seep into cracks in bed-rock, breaking loose and plucking out large chunks as the water freezes and expands. One of the earliest of such boulders to be described is one of limestone, some 60 feet across, reported in 1841 in Switzerland. Most glaciers move their debris, however, by simply bulldozing it ahead of them, or by dragging it along underneath.

A slowly moving, rock-loaded glacier acts like a rasp on the earth. Its

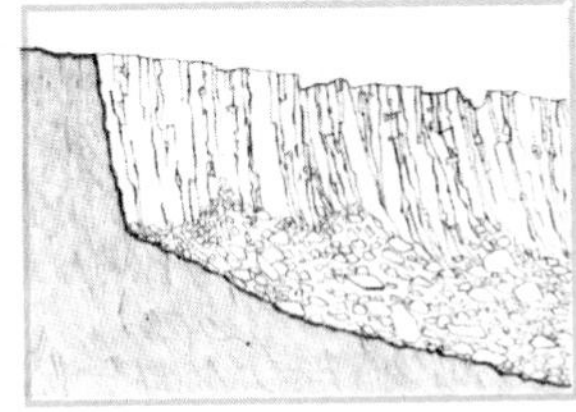

ROCK-FALL

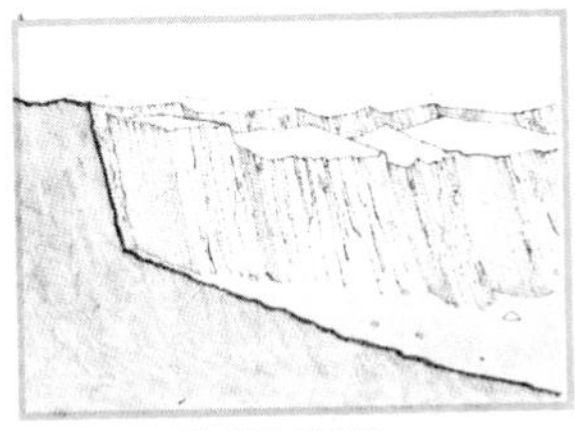

BLOCK GLIDE

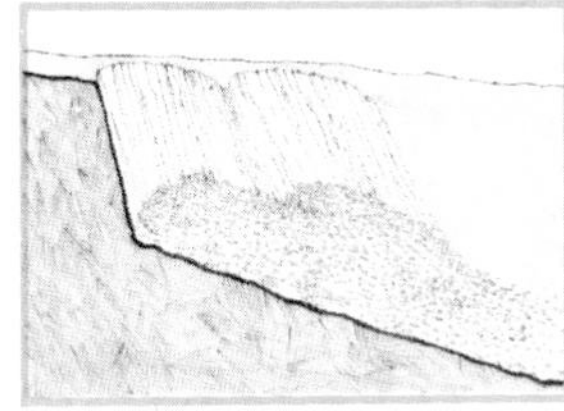

DEBRIS AVALANCHE

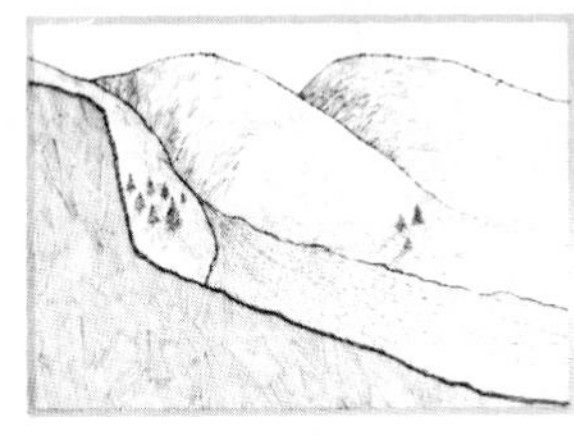

DEBRIS FLOW

LANDSLIDES AND AVALANCHES are examples of erosion in its most spectacular form. A rock-fall (*top*), the most sudden of landslides, occurs when a process of weathering fractures the edge of a cliff, causing it to drop to the ground below. A block glide happens when a large chunk of earth becomes waterlogged at its base and falls by its own weight. A debris avalanche occurs when loose earth on a steep slope becomes wet and slides to the bottom. A debris flow is a river of mud that runs down a valley, usually after a storm.

rough bottom and the loose abrasive material that it drags and pushes shape the sides of mountains and cut U-shaped valleys. If several glaciers work on different sides of a mountain, they sharpen its crest into a point, or "horn". Two glaciers extending from opposite sides of a ridge may join at their heads to cut a narrow, sharp-edged pass. A glacier flowing down a valley plucks rocks most easily from shattered zones and may dig a succession of basins which later fill with water, forming a string of lakes. In the United States, the Finger Lakes of central New York State were scooped out as the last continental ice sheet piled up against the barrier of the Appalachian Plateau to the south. Where bed-rock is exposed, the glacier may polish the surface smooth—and occasionally, like an inept sculptor, leave scratches. There are grooves of this kind two feet deep and three feet wide in the bed-rock at Kelleys Island, in Lake Erie north of Sandusky, Ohio, and others 50 feet deep, 150 feet wide and a mile long in the Mackenzie Valley west of Great Bear Lake, Canada.

In the wake of melting ice

The residue left behind when glaciers melt creates other features of the landscape. The broad plains of north central Germany are composed of glacial silt and sand that settled out of the glacial melt waters which spread over level areas. The boulders littering the valleys of Switzerland and making farming so laborious are "drift" that a glacier pushed and rode over. Long low ridges may be moraines—debris that was either left behind in the sides of valleys along the edges of long-departed glaciers, or had gradually assembled at the point of a glacier's farthest advance. As it melts, it leaves its accumulated pile of sand, gravel and boulders. Some moraines are many hundreds of feet high and contain millions of tons of material.

The isolated lakes often found in Canada were also formed by glaciers. These are known as "kettles", and are depressions left by large blocks of ice that remained frozen long after the rest of the surrounding glacier melted away.

Most mountain glaciers are now in retreat the world over. Whether they will continue to shrink or will grow again to freeze the earth in another ice-age is an open question. But meanwhile water in liquid form continues to mould the land.

It is the energy of the water, its ability to slam and break off things and then to move them around, that does the job. The things that water moves—the sand and rocks—are abrasives that wear away at the surface of the earth.

The effect of this abrasive-in-liquid is perhaps most obvious at the shores of the land, where coastlines are trimmed by waves and currents. The cutting power of their loads of sand and rock can actually be seen

A RIVER'S HISTORY unfolds in a well-defined pattern from the moment of its origin upon a newly upthrust land surface. In its early stage (*left*), it tends to cut a deep and narrow valley, where the flow is small, but on a flat slope downstream where the flow is large, deepening of the channel proceeds more slowly; instead the channel widens the valley. In maturity the river continues to widen its valley, and develops a flat floor, the river flood-plain. On wide flood-plains the river usually develops a meandering pattern.

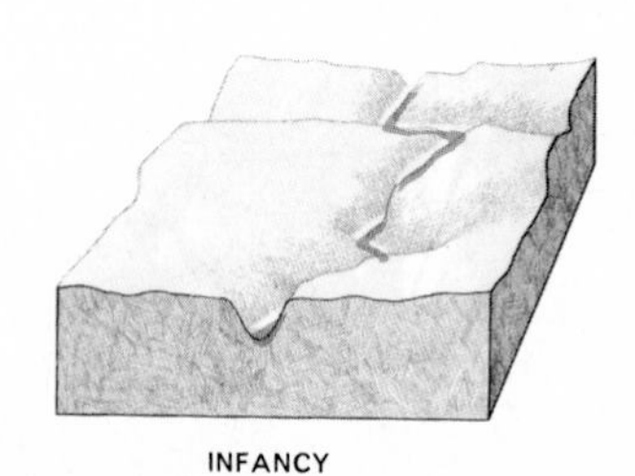
INFANCY

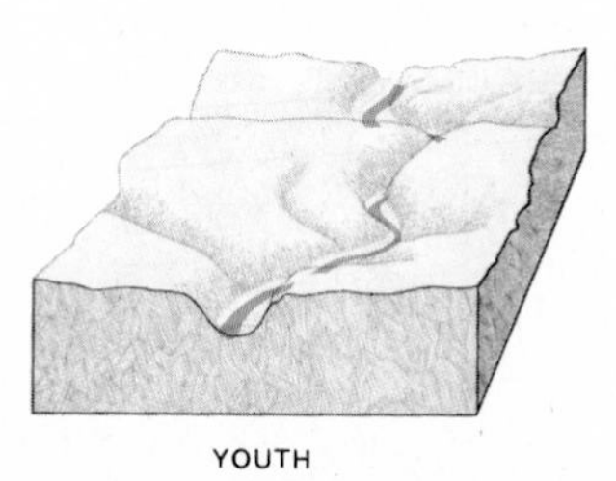
YOUTH

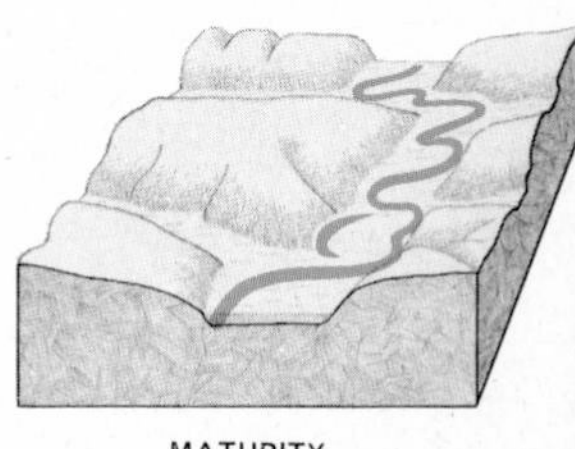
MATURITY

and felt and even heard in action. The surging seas tear down coastlines, cutting back headlands and moving tons of sand. They may wash away a beach completely, only to build a new one somewhere else. This chipping at the contours of the continents is immediate and noticeable, working changes that can be appreciated within the span of a human lifetime. Entire beaches occasionally disappear in a single great storm. New England's famous sandbar peninsular, Cape Cod, a relatively young offspring of the last ice-age, has lost a two-mile-wide strip of land to the waves. At the present rate of erosion the outer Cape will be gone entirely in 4,000 to 5,000 years.

Cliffs on the south shore of Nantucket Island, off Cape Cod, where the waves hurl rocks and rock fragments at the land, lose as much as six feet a year as the abrasive stream undercuts them and causes huge sections to fall into the sea. The grinding and smashing of rock fragments in such a surf fills the air with a distinctive rumble that is easily recognized and, once heard, never forgotten.

Waves often carve a rocky coast into weird forms. They may excavate horizontally under a cliff, then curve upwards to hollow out a cave. The enclosed space sometimes directs the force of the inrushing water upwards to dig at the roof until a hole is torn through. The sea then spouts through the hole like a geyser. A narrow promontory sticking into the ocean may be eroded until a cave breaks through the other side, creating a natural bridge. When, after years of wear, the arch of the bridge falls, the outermost column of rock stands alone, surrounded by water, in the unusual formation called a "stack".

Water, subterranean sculptor

Even more spectacular effects are created on land, by water that acts not as an immense pounding weight but as an inconspicuous yet steady solvent. Perhaps the most dramatic of these are the great caverns which seepage dissolves out of underground limestone. This material, paradoxically, is not soluble in pure water. Rainfall, however, contains some carbon dioxide, absorbed first while dropping through the atmosphere and later while seeping among plant roots. As a result, ground-water becomes dilute carbonic acid and enters into a chemical reaction with limestone, which is mostly calcium carbonate. This reaction converts the insoluble calcium carbonate into calcium bicarbonate, which is quite soluble in water. In submerged crevices, the mild acid eats away the limestone and enlarges the cracks into large rooms and passage-ways. Then water dripping from the ceiling begins to ornament it with beautiful, icicle-like stalactites, and with stalagmites rising up from the floor. Their formation, too, depends on the calcium-carbonate/calcium-bicarbonate reaction: when a solution of bicarbonate evaporates, it releases carbon dioxide

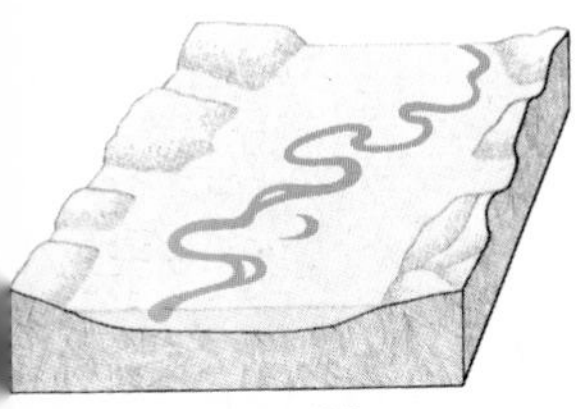
LATE MATURITY

and the residue reverts to the carbonate—limestone. The drops which cling to a cavern ceiling are rich solutions of calcium bicarbonate; when they evaporate they deposit on the ceiling a microscopic quantity of limestone. Similarly, when a drop that falls to the floor evaporates, it adds a speck of limestone there. And so the stalactites grow down, the stalagmites grow up.

Caverns formed and decorated in this way are to be found in nearly all the great limestone districts of the world: Italy, Greece, Yugoslavia, France, Spain, Australia, the Yucatan in Mexico, Cuba, Puerto Rico and the eastern United States. In the south-western U.S., the Carlsbad labyrinth in south-eastern New Mexico, which has still not been completely explored, is deeper than 1,100 feet and contains one irregular chamber that is 280 feet high and contains 14 acres of floor area.

When underground caverns collapse they often make surface hollows, or "sinks". The earth's surface, when dotted with such sinks, forms a strangely topsy-turvy landscape called karst topography, after a region in Yugoslavia where such sinks are particularly common. The valleys widen and narrow abruptly, walled at one end, and sometimes at both, by vertical cliffs; sizeable rivers suddenly disappear into the earth; deep depressions are arched by natural bridges of stone; branch valleys hang unfinished, having been robbed of the water which was cutting them.

Force in falling raindrops

Water usually forms landscape not so much by dissolving earth as by carrying it as waterborne debris. Rain tears away at the earth's surface with a power that is astonishing. The power of the drops striking one acre in a heavy rain of one inch per hour is equivalent to that of a 100 horsepower car engine running at top speed. A very heavy rain—two inches an hour—expends enough energy in one hour to lift a seven-inch layer of that acre 258 feet into the air.

Each raindrop is a miniature hammer, breaking off minute fragments from the hardest rock. Striking loose dirt, it gouges holes and splashes particles into the air. The water collects other particles within itself, forming a muddy suspension that often clogs the surface pores of the ground. This puddling prevents the rain that follows from sinking into the ground and causes it to accumulate in sheets over the surface. In a pelting rain, the sheets of water are churned, greatly increasing the capacity of the subsequent run-off to dislodge, lift and transport soil and rock materials. These materials further augment erosion by acting as abrasives that scour and cut the ground. The run-off trickles its bit of the land into the nearest streams. The streams tear at their courses and dump their burden into the river. The river continues the process. From the stuff of mountains and foot-hills the river constructs the lowlands—the flood-plains, the broad alluvial valleys, the delta thrusting into the sea.

Despite the importance of the rivers to mankind, only now is a mathematical theory of river science being developed. New concepts, based on energy relations, reveal a remarkable unit underlying all the world's river systems, and are leading to a deeper understanding of such ancient problems as floods, silting, erosion and channel-shifting.

A long-lasting view of landscape sculpture was developed in the 1880's by the American William Morris Davis, an ebullient geologist of forceful personality. Davis saw rivers and their valleys as living organisms that grew from infancy through youth and maturity to old age. According to Davis, the life cycle of a river begins when new land is raised above the sea. Rain runs down and gullies it; the gullies run together to form river channels. Lakes collect in the low spots of the uneven surface but soon disappear as shallow streams deepen their channels and cut downwards to form steep-sided, V-shaped valleys. Tributaries then grow from the main trunk of the river like branches from a tree. As the river matures, its valleys deepen and the tributaries lengthen.

From vigorous maturity to sluggish age

During this period, Davis said, when the greatest amount of sloping surface is exposed to erosion, the river carries away its greatest load of earth. The lower trunk stream, flowing down a gentle slope, may not be able to transport so much and therefore lays some of it aside in a floodplain. Almost imperceptibly, the river passes from vigorous maturity into old age. All the valley slopes have been much reduced; the once steeply concave river basin becomes a shallow dish, and the now sluggish river, its surface only slightly above sea level, carries less sediment.

Davis's biological metaphor was persuasive and continues to be used today. But to it has been added the detailed understanding which came from field measurement. One pioneer in statistical analysis of such measurements was an American engineer, very different from Davis, named Robert E. Horton. A tall, lanky man with a tremendous shock of white hair that stood up from the top of his head as if pulled by lightning, Horton enjoyed a long and highly remunerative career as a consulting hydraulic engineer. His statistical description of river systems was one of the first indications of the elementary mathematics that relates all rivers everywhere in the world. He classified rivers as to size according to the complexity of their tributaries. A stream with no tributaries is designated as one of the first order. A river with one or more first-order tributaries is a stream of the second order. The river becomes third order only when it acquires at least one second-order tributary, and so on. The Mississippi is about 10th order, and the Amazon and Congo, largest rivers in the world, are variously classified as 12th or 13th order.

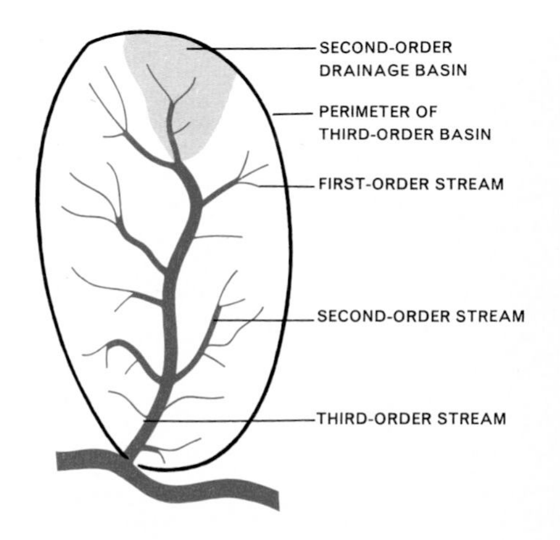

A DRAINAGE BASIN, the region which feeds a river system, is part of a geological hierarchy that ranks all rivers according to the kinds of streams feeding them. In this ranking, a first-order stream is one that has no tributaries, rising entirely from a spring or from precipitation. A second-order stream is fed by first-order streams. Shown here is a third-order stream; its drainage basin consists solely of second- and first-order streams (a second-order drainage basin is shown in light blue). This method of ranking streams was developed during the 1940's by Robert Horton, an American hydraulic engineer.

As might be expected, nearly every river system on earth includes fewer high-order than low-order streams. As the order increases, so does the length of the river, and so do both the total number of streams that feed into it and the area of the watershed that they drain. More surprising is the mathematical relationship that determines how many tributaries of each order a stream will possess. It turns out that the average stream has three or four tributaries of the next smaller order.

That is, a second-order stream is fed by three or four first-order creeks, and a tenth-order river is fed by three or four ninth-order rivers. The Potomac is estimated to be seventh-order; its tributaries of approximately sixth order are the Shenandoah, the northern and southern branches of the Potomac, and the Monocacy.

When these broad relationships became apparent, they suggested how basic physical laws govern the operation of rivers. This led Walter B. Langbein and his colleagues of the U.S. Geological Survey to compare a river to an energy system. A river contains energy gained when its water was evaporated from the sea and lifted into the atmosphere. This is energy of position—the same as that gained by a weight which is lifted off the floor. If the weight is dropped, the energy of position is converted into energy of motion—that is, into the velocity of the falling weight. And finally the energy of motion is dissipated in the impact when the falling weight hits the floor. In exactly the same way, some of the position energy of atmospheric moisture is converted into motion energy and then dissipated on impact when raindrops fall. But many of the fallen raindrops still retain position energy because they land at elevations above sea level; they have not dropped all the way to the "floor". This remaining position energy passes into the water of streams and rivers. It is spent gradually—converted into heat by various kinds of friction—as the water courses downhill, until finally all the position energy is used up when the river reaches the sea. The slope of the downward-flowing water surface is a measure of the energy loss along the stream length.

The thermodynamics of flowing rivers

A similar dissipation of energy occurs in a heat cycle, such as that taking place in a steam-engine, and this has led Langbein to apply the mathematical equations of thermodynamics to rivers. These equations specify two facts involving the rates at which energy is lost: first, the rate of loss must be fairly evenly distributed along the channel so that every unit of bed area assumes an equal share in the energy loss. That is, the river rubs about as hard on one spot as it does on the next. Although exactly equal distribution is rarely achieved, a concentration of energy loss is also rare—it occurs, for example, when a fire hose kinks and the full force of the stream of water is exerted at that single point.

Secondly, these rates of loss of energy, when added up for all parts of the river system, must be as low as possible. This simply means that the river, taken as a whole, expends its energy as slowly as it can. When it is found to expend energy at a great rate, as at a waterfall, it attempts to redress the balance by wearing down the waterfall.

These two requirements of the theory—minimum rates of loss and uniform distribution of loss—conflict with each other. The slope of the river course that best suits one will not suit the other. There has to be an adjustment. As a result, the river never achieves either uniform distribution or minimum rate of loss anywhere, but trades one requirement off against the other, like a housewife balancing a skimpy budget.

The practical outcome of these theoretical considerations can be seen in familiar situations. Because of the uniform-distribution requirement, the kinked fire hose will not stay kinked: the concentration of energy at the kink forces the hose to untwist itself into a gentle curve. A waterfall quickly wears its precipice down into a sloping valley because of the combination of requirements: the sudden drop at the falls constitutes both a high rate of loss and a concentrated loss; erosion tends to provide a more uniform distribution, exemplified by the usually gentle slope of the valley.

A tendency to wander

A more complex demonstration of these effects is provided by rivers' tendency to meander. Unless they are hemmed in by the hand of man, all streams will flow in curves: natural channels are seldom straight for a distance of more than 10 channel-widths. Thus, a stream 100 feet wide will have straight stretches no longer than about a thousand feet.

Meandering seems to be characteristic of all streams. Its immediate cause, it has been suggested, is the undulating surface of the channel bottom. A river bed is not a flat trough but an alternating series of pools and riffles established by incoming sediment deposits. The sediment flows in at random but the particles quickly sort themselves into bunches—like cars forming platoons on a busy highway. This bunching action creates the riffles, with pools in between.

Water flows steeply downwards over a riffle, expending more energy per unit length than could be dissipated in the level pool behind it—unless balancing effects intervene. To compensate for the lack of slope in the pool and increase the loss per unit length there, the water is forced to change its direction and travel around a curve. Thus the river balances its accounts, keeping energy loss uniform and minimum. The mathematics of the theory explains a fact visible to any observer: meandering rivers curve at their pools and run straight over their riffles.

Meandering is more noticeable in flat valleys, where banks erode easily, than in rocky, steep mountains. The curves follow a pattern of their own, a series of arcs extending over about five to seven channel-widths. That is, the curved sections of a river 100 feet wide will contain an average of 8 to 10 curves per mile. Their shape is also characteristic, not a circular arc but a specialized trigonometric curve, which keeps total bending to a minimum for a given length—precisely the curve assumed by an unkinking fire hose.

Eventually the rivers—small or large, famous or obscure—reach the sea, their energy spent. They deposit in their deltas the last of the land they have torn away. And finally they mix into the currents of the ocean and help to shape its basins until, once more, some of their waters are beckoned by the sun to rise as vapour—to return again to the landforms that are never quite the same as they were a million years ago, last month or even yesterday.

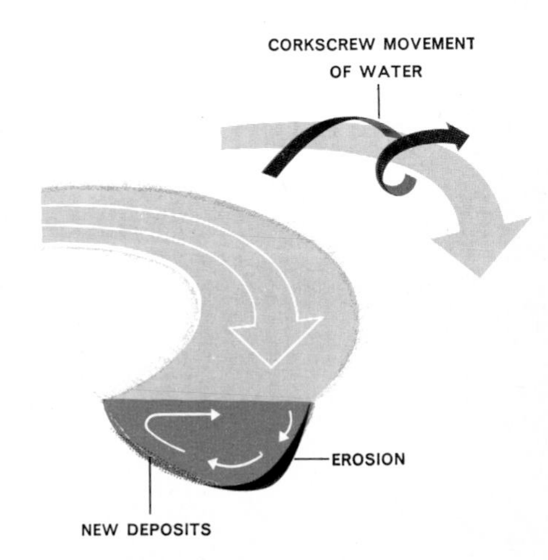

SHIFTING ITS COURSE, a river moves sideways where it curves because of the way its water erodes and deposits bed material. Water rounding the curve is subjected to centrifugal force. The water at the bottom, retarded by friction, moves more slowly than the surface water. These influences combine to give a corkscrew movement to the water. As a result, silt picked up at the outer bank is deposited on the inner bank, slowly causing an increase in the curve's arc.

How Erosion Makes Landscapes

Ever since the earth's crust began forming, about 4,000 million years ago, water has been wearing it away. Erosion has scarred and sculpted the earth's surface with mountains, chasms, deserts and deltas. Rivers and rainfall, glaciers and waves, dew and frost, all participate in the process. Yet, despite the variety of erosive agents, certain patterns of erosion are visible everywhere in the earth's features. In any given environment the slopes of hills will always be about the same: the slopes of the Swiss Alps are almost uniform; so are the desert slopes of Iran. All rivers share common profiles, cutting mountain gorges, meandering over flood-plains and building deltas. In the same way, the pattern of drainage channels cut into the earth by rainfall remains basically constant. These similarities occur because whenever water works on the land, it always tries to expand its energy at a constant rate. For this reason it abhors obstacles, wearing them down in much the same fashion wherever it finds them. If water had its way, all landscapes would be the same, and all streams would flow at an even rate on an unobstructed journey to the sea.

WATER-MARKED MOUNTAINS

The ridges, ribbed slopes and canyons of the Henry Mountains in Utah have been cut by the run-off of rain-water over many aeons. About 80 million years ago a barren shale plain stretched over the land where the mountains now stand. The mountains thrust up through this plain were originally dome-shaped, but erosive streams have cut the shale caps down to the present pattern.

The Changing Face of the Land

No crag or cranny of the earth escapes the irresistible force of water as it flows from mountains to sea. Erosion works on all principal geologic forms, as illustrated in the fanciful landscape on the right. Flowing glaciers, meandering rivers and crashing waves combine with subtler weathering processes to carve valleys, flatten plains, straighten coastlines.

Where water meets the most resistance, it works the hardest. On mountain slopes, torrential streams (and occasionally glaciers) cut down through rock, the earth's most resistant form. On more gently sloping plains, water meanders in broad swaths over soft soil, depositing as much material as it erodes. If it were not for this balance of erosion and resistance, the earth might rapidly be reduced to an inhospitable terrain of sheer precipices and deep chasms.

Over great geologic ages, another sort of balance is struck—between erosion and rebuilding of mountains. The Appalachians of the eastern U.S. have had seven face-liftings in the past 200 million years, upraised by the earth's intense churnings and then cut down by millennia of rainfall. Were it not for this erosion, the chain's tallest peaks would tower a mile higher than Mount Everest.

THE FEATURES OF EROSION
The many interactions of water and landforms are shown in this composite landscape. Across the foreground, waves wear away at a sandy coast. In the mountains in the rear, glaciers scoop out valleys, while hills (*far right*) are stripped of their covering soil by drainage. Streams and rivers (*centre*) carry sediment to the sea. In desert regions (*middle right*), water carves out rocky canyons and cuts away plateaux of softer clay. Cliffs are cut back by the flooding of near-by rivers. The changes that might be wrought in 10,000 years of such weathering are shown in a matching illustration on pages 100-101.

MOUNTAIN PEAKS
RIDGED MOUNTAINS
PLATEAU
CANYON
ARROYO
BADLANDS
DRAINAGE BASIN
TRIBUTARY
CLIFFS
SALT LAKE
MEANDER
SEDIMENT
FLOOD-PLAIN
COASTAL PLAIN
DELTA
WAVE-CUT CLIFFS

The Force of Frozen Water

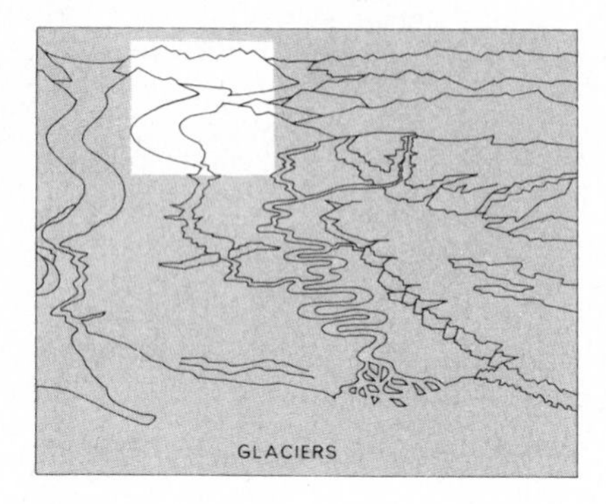

Glaciers, colossal masses of ice capable of grinding up mountains, form where freezing temperatures permit the packing-down of the snows of many years. In Greenland, 10,000 centuries of snow have formed an ice-cap 10,000 feet high. Under so much snow, internal pressure may reach seven tons to the square foot. The bottom layers of ice become so compressed that they begin to flow, as illustrated in the diagram below.

On the right, a photographic detail of the larger picture on the preceding pages shows a glacier (white square in diagram on the left) thus set in motion. It flows in much the same fashion as a river, although it may take centuries to creep down a mountain valley. Tremendous amounts of rock are ground to a fine flour as the glacier gouges the land. Streams melting out of the lower reaches of glaciers on Mont Blanc in France carry off some 70,000 tons of debris a year.

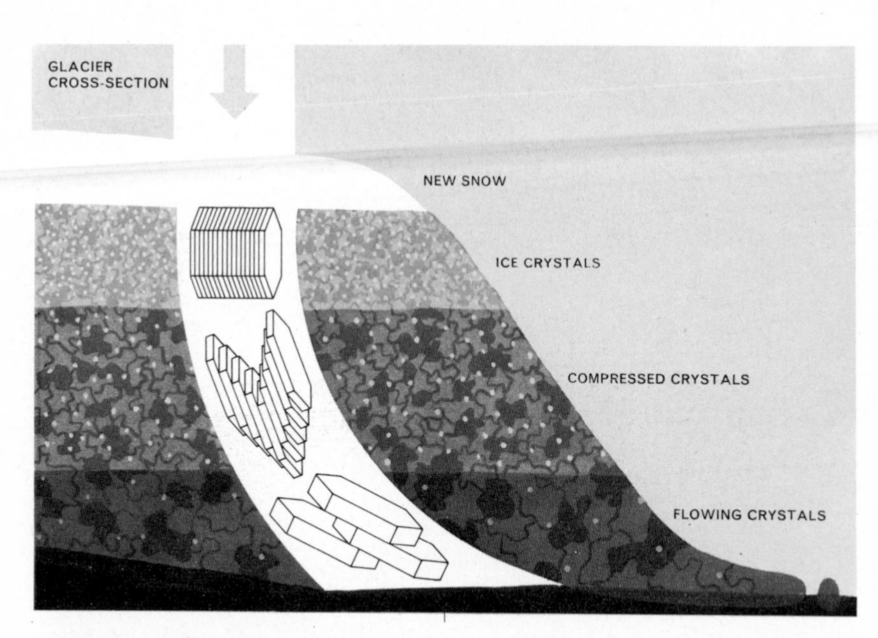

PRESSURE THAT MAKES SOLIDS FLOW

Glaciers flow, according to the current accepted theory, because their great weight alters the molecular structure of the ice. Each ice crystal consists of 60 water molecules grouped in hexagonal layers, seen near the top. Internal pressure distorts the crystals, causing layers to slip; at the base of the glacier, the pressure becomes so great that the crystal layers flow freely

VAST RIVERS OF ICE

The long ribbon of Kaskawulsh Glacier in the St. Elias Mountains in the Yukon flows like a winding highway between rocky peaks. Debris cut from the edges of outcrops is carried away, forming the long dark lines of crushed rock, called moraines, visible in the picture above.

Drops and Crystals That Split Rock

Some of the most dramatic changes effected by water are accomplished by processes too minute to be seen with the unaided eye. A single drop of rain may pound the soil with a force of 2.3 pounds per square inch (in an average downpour, some five million drops fall on every acre every second). A single crystal of ice lodged in a rock pore, formed as moisture is frozen, expands with a pressure of 400 pounds per square inch; multiplied by a great number of crystals, this is enough to split the rock. A crystal of salt left behind by evaporating water grows in crevices of rock, expanding until the rock is fractured. Water also exerts a profound chemical force on the earth. Certain elements abundant in ground-water, rain and dew react on minerals in rock, dissolving it into soil, and in some cases creating plant foods.

If water can destroy rock in many ways, it can also rebuild it. Three-quarters of the surface of the earth is now covered with layers of sedimentary rock, which are built out of compressed material washed away from one place and redeposited in another.

A raindrop pounds the wet soil, loosening particles. This photograph, taken at 1/1,000 of a second, has been greatly magnified.

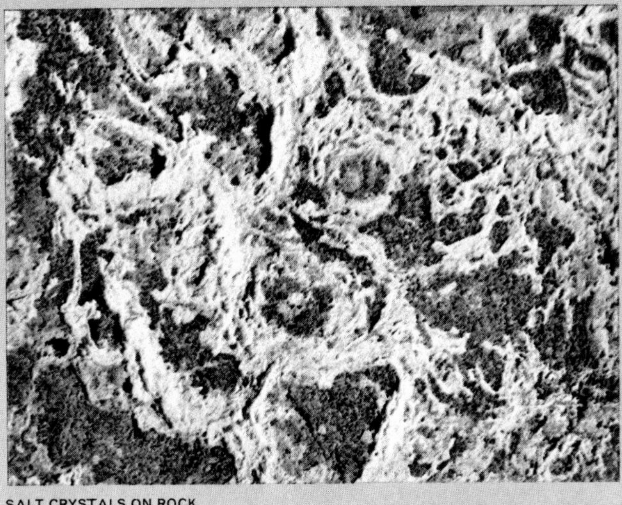

SALT CRYSTALS ON ROCK

SOIL IN SNOW-BANK

DEW ON ROCK

ICE-SHATTERED ROCK

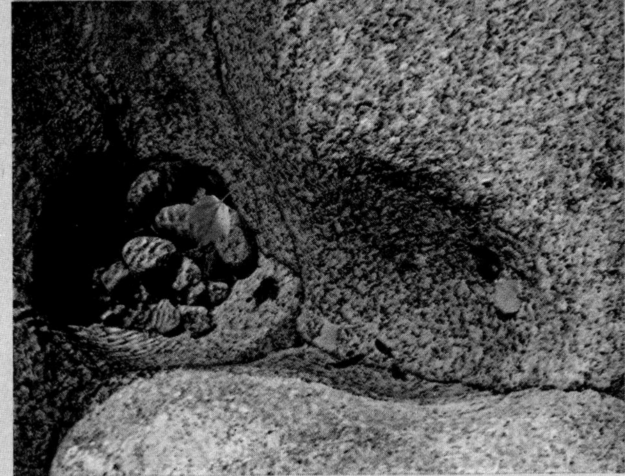

POT-HOLE IN GRANITE

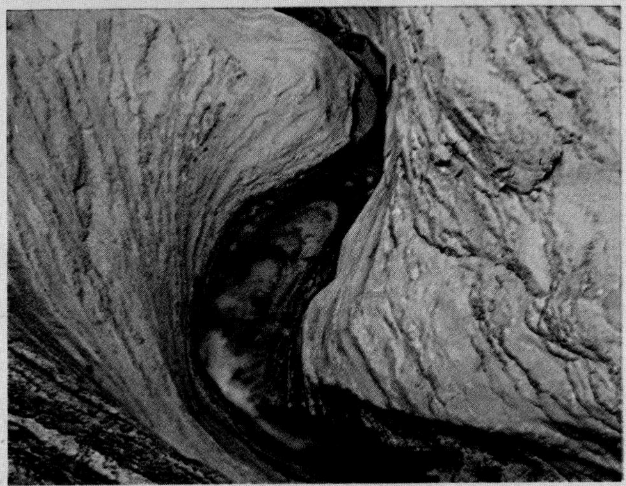

CHANNEL IN LIMESTONE

THE BEGINNINGS OF EROSION

Many common features of the land, like those shown in these photographs, reveal erosion in progress. At the upper left, a slab of basalt is encrusted with salt crystals formed as moisture evaporated. Growing in crevices, the salt crystals can split the rock. At the upper right, a snow-bank is caked with soil it has picked up from the ground. As the snow melts, the soil is washed away. At the middle left, a granite boulder is streaked with trickling dew. The granite decomposes as carbon dioxide dissolved in the dew reacts with the mineral feldspar in the rock, changing the feldspar to clay. At the middle right, the face of a granite cliff, shattered with irregular cracks, shows the effect of frost on solid rock. The cracks are caused by expanding ice crystals lodged in pores of the rock. The bottom pictures show two different ways in which flowing water erodes rock. At the left, a stream digs a deep pot-hole into granite rock as it swirls against the surface: small pebbles, called grinders, caught up in the current, scrape against the rock, milling it down. At the right, water flows through a channel in limestone, cut into the rock by chemical action. Carbon dioxide dissolved in the water reacts with the mineral calcite in limestone to decompose the rock.

A Self-built Drainage System

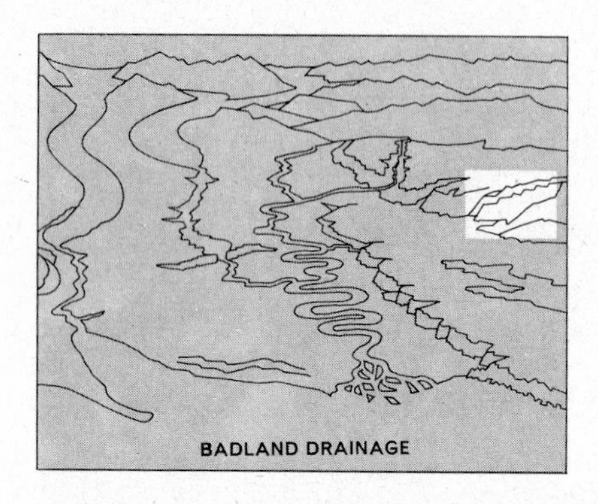

Wherever rainfall runs off the land, it dredges its own drainage system—and the pattern of rills and channels it leaves behind is always the same. Smaller channels drain into larger ones in a tree-like arrangement of branches until all the surface water empties into a main trunk. On a small scale this pattern can be seen in the gullies that drain an acre or two; on a large scale, the same pattern applies to the tributaries that empty into a river. In this way the Mississippi and its extensive branching network of tributaries drain a region of 1,250,000 square miles, emptying 724,000 million cubic feet of water a year into the Gulf of Mexico.

Although the pattern is constant, the number of drainage channels in a region varies with the amount of rainfall and nature of the soil. In semi-arid areas, more than 40 small stream channels may drain only about 4 acres; on a mountain slope the same number may drain 4,000 acres.

This basic pattern is constant because the tree-like arrangement of channels or tributaries is the most efficient: any other system would require a greater total length of channel (i.e., the combined length of all the branches) to drain the same area. Thus, in constructing its own drainage ditches, water works everywhere to make the least work for itself.

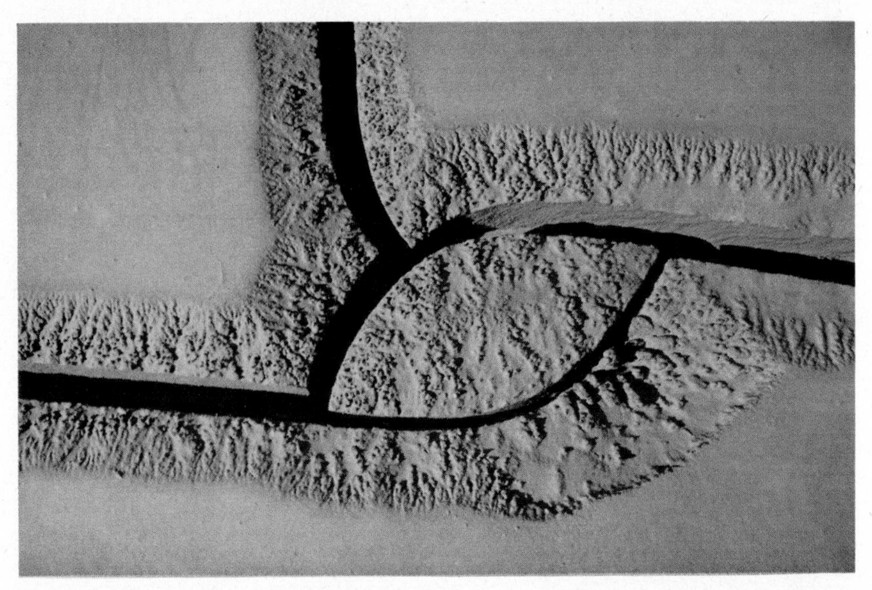

CHANNELS IN DRIED SILT

Cracks in a silt bed occur as the sun dries out the surface moisture. With each rainfall, water running down from the upturned edges of the cracks carves a series of small, tree-shaped rills and channels—a pattern seen on a larger scale on the sides of rocks below (*right, foreground*).

CHANNELS IN ANCIENT ROCK

The easily erodable clays of the Painted Desert in Arizona are extensively sculptured with drainage rills and channels. On the entire Colorado Plateau, of which this area is a part, an estimated 1,000 million million tons of rock has been eroded during the last 13 million years.

Waterfalls—Giant Self-Wreckers

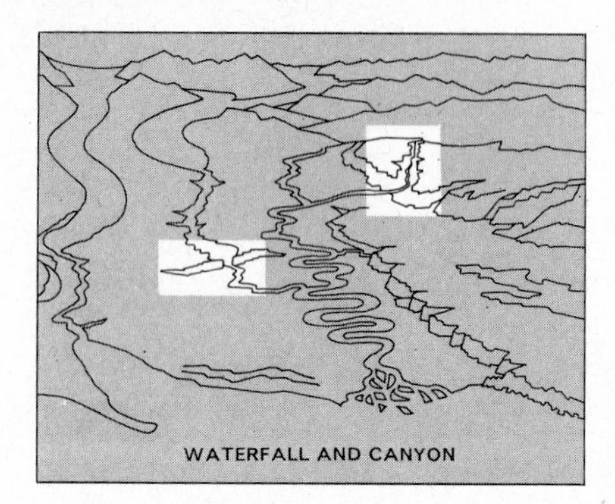

Waterfalls are, in a sense, great accidents of erosion. Where a river abruptly crosses from hard to soft rock, the soft rock—an ancient lava flow, for example—is rapidly worn down, leaving a lip or waterfall. Niagara Falls on the U.S. Canadian border was created in this fashion. Where a river cuts down into its bed faster than does a tributary, the tributary is left hanging, with a waterfall connecting the two. Occasionally, a river flows over an underground cavern and cuts it open, creating a waterfall at the site.

However it may be formed, a waterfall is an aberration. Ordinarily, a river expends its energy more or less steadily, not too much at any one point along its course. But at a waterfall, great quantities of energy are dissipated at an extravagant rate. As soon as a waterfall is formed, however, water power goes to work to erode the falls and restore the river's original, less precipitous bed. The water dropping over Niagara digs great plunge pools at the base, undermining the shale cliff and causing the hard, limestone cap to cave in. Niagara has eaten itself seven miles upstream since it was formed 10,000 years ago. At this rate, it will disappear into Lake Erie in 22,800 years.

WASHING AWAY THE ROCK
The river Iguazú plunges off 180-million-year-old lava beds at the Iguazú Falls on the Brazil-Argentina border. A hard-rock cap at the top is undermined by the churning water (an average of 44,000 cubic feet per second). With occasional cave-ins, the falls recede upstream.

WIDENING A GORGE
The 20-mile canyon gouged 1,200 feet deep through soft, volcanic rock of the Yellowstone Plateau has been left behind by Yellowstone Falls (at the canyon's head) as it has slowly inched its way upstream. Since the canyon was carved out, smaller drainage streams have continued to strip covering rock from its sides, slowly increasing the width of the entire gorge.

In its wanderings, Alabama's Black Warrior river has curved so far that it has looped back on itself; when this happens, the river flow bypasses

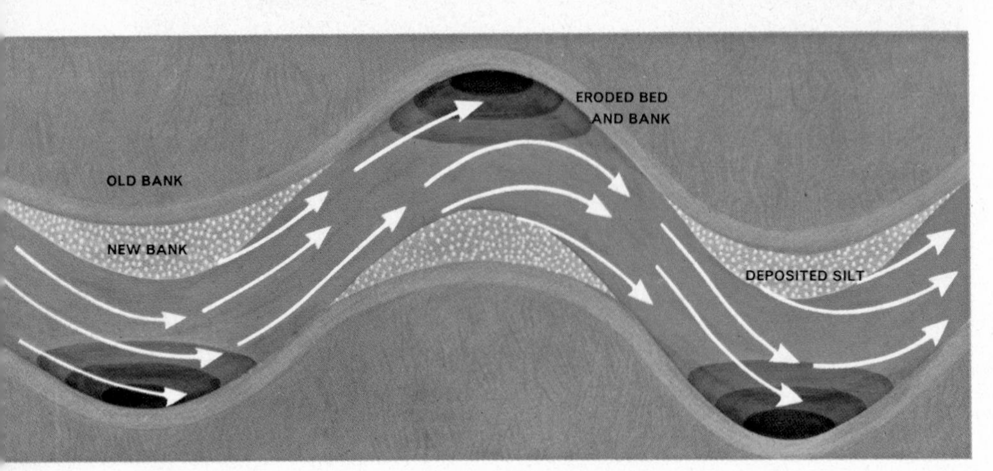

CUTTING SHARPER CURVES
As a river cuts a meandering course across a plain, the water at its surface, represented by the arrows, crosses in a diagonal path from one bank to the next. Some of this water collides with the bank and erodes it; some is forced down and erodes the bed. Material from the eroded area (*dark blue*) is deposited downstream (*beige*) on the same side. Thus, at each curve, one bank is cut away, one built up, and the net result is that the river curves more sharply.

the loop, which forms an oxbow lake (*centre*).

Deltas Built on Dumping Grounds

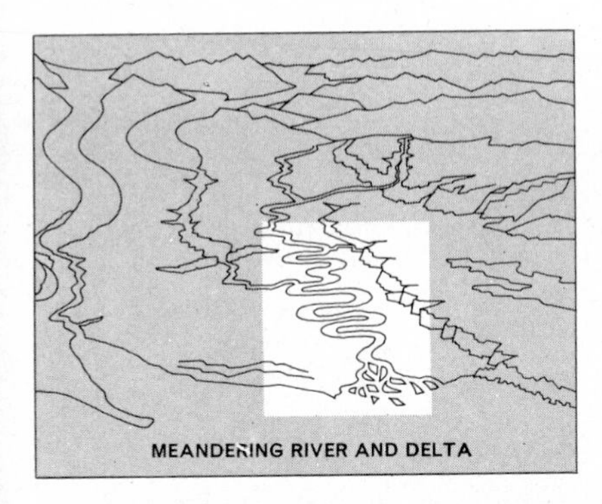

On a level flood-plain, a river often flows over a bed of its own creation. The plain is built up with layers of silt deposited in the course of the river's restless meanderings, or during its floods. A single grain of silt may take thousands of years to move from mountain peak to sea. Eroded material is washed along in a series of short hops—a grain of silt may be swept downstream for several days, then sit lodged in a bank for several thousand years before its next hop. Where a river empties into a lake or the sea, its velocity is checked and it dumps a heavy load of silt to the bottom. As the silt accumulates, a river mouth becomes a new delta of land.

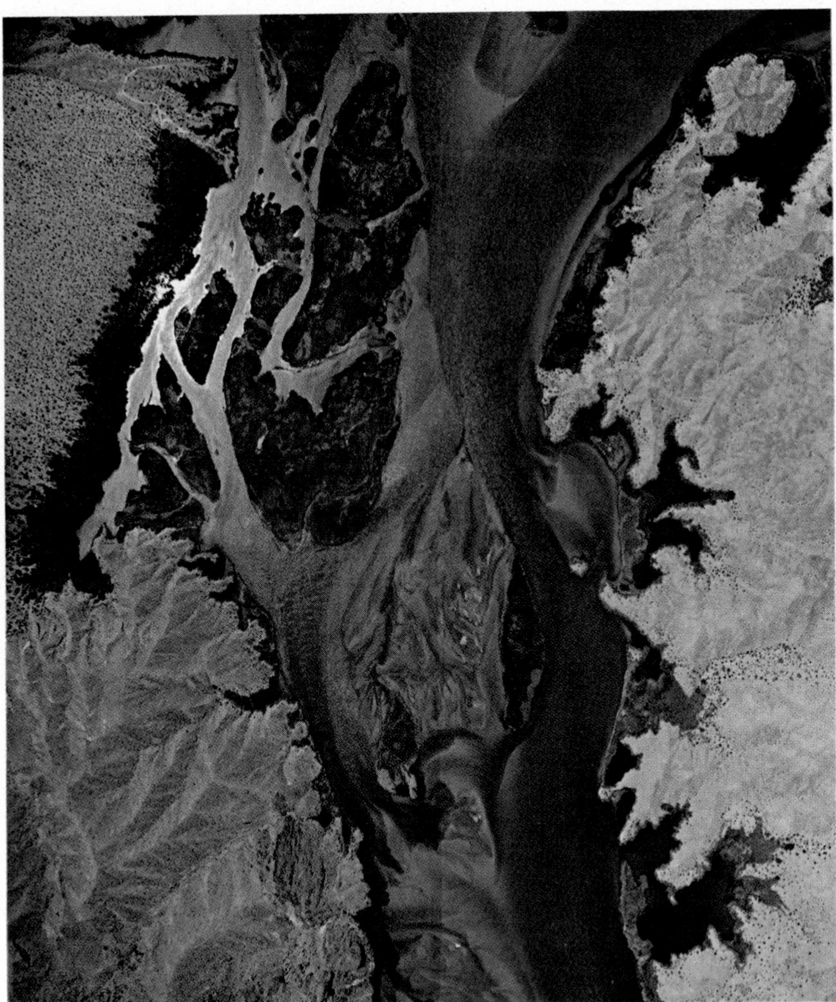

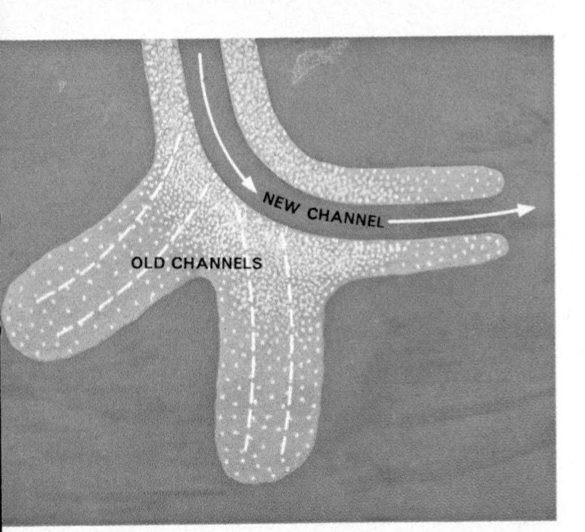

THE CONSTRUCTION OF A DELTA
The river Colorado carries its load of silt downstream into Lake Havasu at the California-Arizona border (*above*), building a fan-shaped area of land at the river mouth. Such deltas are formed (*left*) wherever flowing water meets a body of still water; when this occurs, deposited sediment builds up, forcing the main flow of the river or creek to a new channel. The Mississippi drops 1¾ million tons of sediment a day into the Gulf of Mexico, a load so great that its weight is actually deforming the crust of the earth—causing it to sag at the rate of three feet a century.

Straightening Crooked Coastlines

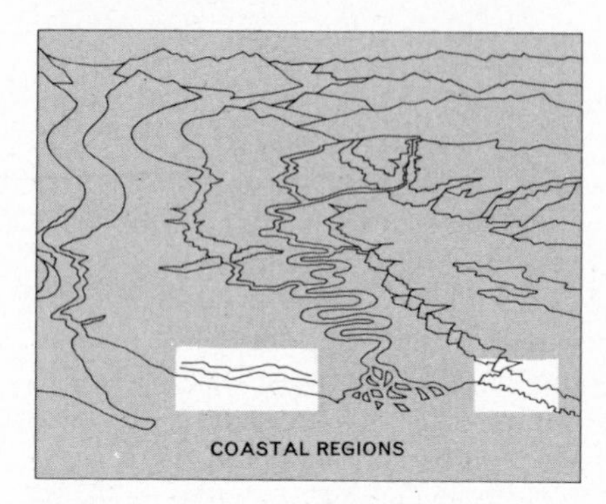

Smashing against the shore with tremendous energy, ocean waves slowly erode the most jagged coast to a smooth, straight shoreline. A wave 10 feet high hits the coast with 1,675 pounds of pressure per square foot. A storm wave 18 feet high can move 10-ton blocks of stone. As the wind whips a wave towards the coast, it moves in a straight front. Where a beach is uneven, however, a wave is bent around the jutting headland—and most of its force is brought to bear on that point (*below and right*). Just as a beach is straightened, the promontory of a cliff, receiving the brunt of a wave's erosive force (*far right*), is eventually worn smooth. Thus a wave erodes any coastline at the point of most resistance. It is the same principle by which water works everywhere—straightening and levelling, eroding and rebuilding, until it need expend as small amount of energy in one place as in another.

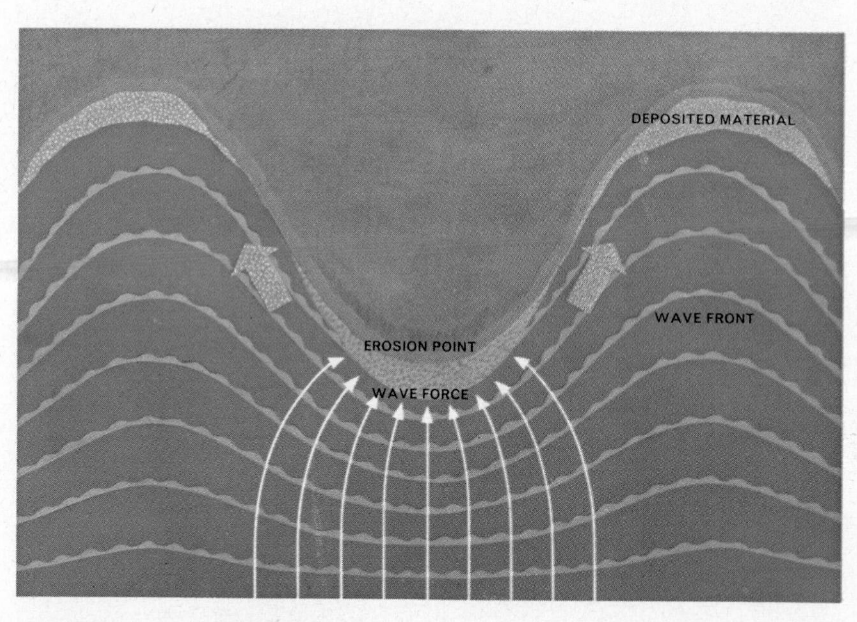

FLATTENING A PROJECTION
A coastal headland creates the conditions for its own erosion by causing the waves to bend around it. The force a wave exerts (*arrows*) is always focused at right angles to the wave front (*blue lines*). As the wave bends around a point, its force is concentrated, or bunched, at the point, thus causing the most erosion there. Where the shore is recessed, forces are diffused.

EVIDENCE OF AGE-OLD SHORES
Gentle waves lap against a central California beach (*right*), as the breakers in the background erode the headland. The rocky ledges or marine terraces on the hill above the beach are actually old shorelines, raised as the rock was thrust up from sea level over succeeding centuries.

CLIFF-CUTTING WAVES
Waves splash against an outcropping of volcanic rock in the British West Indies. The water erodes the rock at sea level; eventually, this rocky obstacle will be entirely washed away.

10,000 Years of Erosion

Although a rampaging flood or a disastrous drought, striking within a relatively brief time, may leave a local blemish on the earth's features, most of the massive changes wrought by water's erosion can be measured only over millennia. Part of the reason for this is that only a small fraction of water's energy is expended on effectively eroding soil and rock. If all the potential energy of the water in the United States were put to work, it would provide power equivalent to five million bulldozers working around the clock.

The landscape on the right, showing the same geologic formations as in the matching illustration on pages 86-87, depicts the changes that might actually occur after 10,000 years—a span of time equal to that from the Stone Age to the present. This is a short period in geologic terms—the Rocky Mountains, for example, took more than 70 million years to form. But even in 10,000 years a great deal of water-engineering goes on. For one thing, in 100 centuries enough water will have run down the river Mississippi to fill eight Gulfs of Mexico, carrying enough sediment to build a mountain taller than Mount Everest.

THE WEATHERED LANDSCAPE
Compared with the way the same landscape looked 10,000 years earlier, the terrain on the right has undergone considerable change. Mountain glaciers (*background*) have retreated as the climate has warmed; the coastline (*foreground*), straightened at the centre, has been pushed out on the right by the formation of a delta; the mountain peaks (*right background*) are somewhat reduced, the valleys deepened. The meandering course of rivers (*centre*) has created a variety of oxbow lakes. On the plain, one lake has evaporated into a salt bed, another has been absorbed into a gorge, and the badlands have receded.

MOUNTAIN PEAKS
RIDGE MOUNTAINS
REDUCED PLATEAU
CANYON
MESA
NEW GORGE
EXTENDED MEANDERS
RECESSED BADLANDS
NEW VALLEY
FLOOD-PLAIN
SALT DEPOSITS
TRIBUTARY
FILLED-IN
OXBOW LAKE
OXBOW LAKE
CLIFFS
SEDIMENT
WAVE-CUT CLIFFS
COASTAL PLAIN
ERODED OUTCROPS
ENLARGED DELTA

5

Fountain of Life

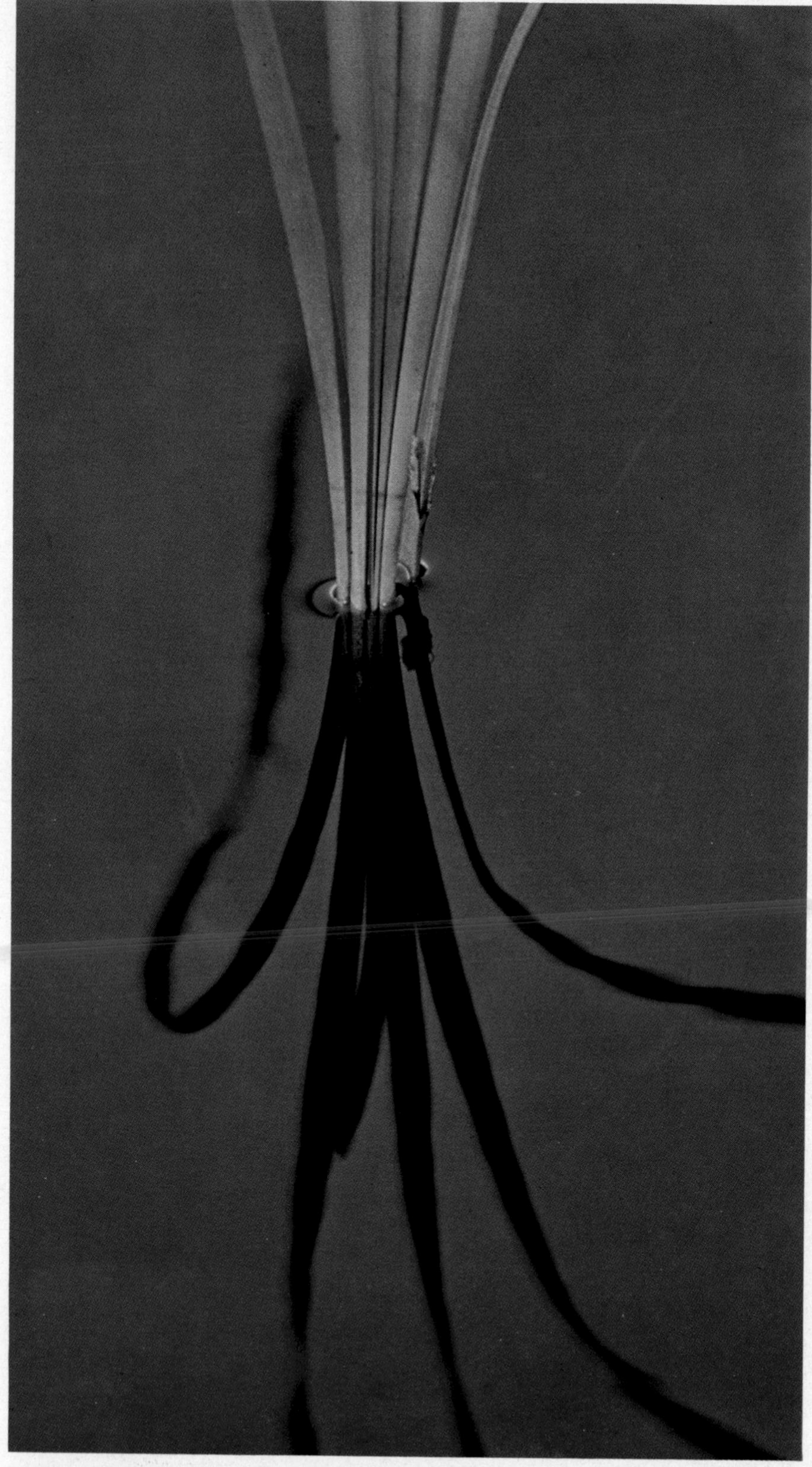

DRAWING LIFE FROM THE SURROUNDING FLOOD, A WATER-LOVING CAT-TAIL RISES FROM THE SURFACE OF A SWAMP.

"The waters of life" is more than a poetic phrase. Life actually arose in water, to start the long line of evolution that links primitive animals and plants, which are virtually nothing but water, to man, who is two-thirds water. Before birth, much of man's life is spent in water, in the sheltering membranous sac of his mother's womb, and water flows through his body till the day he dies. Man can live several weeks without food; one Indian fakir survived 81 days with no nourishment whatever. But without water, the longest any human being can expect to live is 10 days. Some bacteria flourish without oxygen, but neither they nor any other form of life can grow without water. It defies barriers to penetrate the living cells of plants and animals, and it overcomes gravity to climb the highest trees, bringing nutrients to their topmost branches.

The earth's water was there when the planet was formed. It lay in the oceans before the present atmosphere was created, and it was this circumstance, according to one theory, that led to the development of life. Today the oxygen in the atmosphere absorbs much of the sun's ultra-violet radiation. But aeons ago this energetic portion of the solar spectrum beat down uninterruptedly on the great primeval seas. Mixed with the water in those days were substantial quantities of ammonia, methane and carbon dioxide—providing all the chemical elements necessary to give rise to living molecules. The powerful ultra-violet radiation may have stimulated the arrangement and rearrangement of these elements into one pattern after another until finally, purely by chance, compounds that could duplicate themselves were formed. If such random syntheses, stimulated by the sun and supported by the water, continued over hundreds of millions of years, life could have evolved. (The theory is supported by recent experiments which reproduced on a laboratory scale the presumed conditions of the ancient seas—and yielded complex chemicals that are the precursors of living protein.)

Life's watery beginning continues to be reflected in all living processes, plant and animal. The simplest single-celled organisms are surrounded by and permeated with water. It moves in and out of their walls, bringing food and oxygen along and taking wastes away. The principle is the same but the processes are more complicated in higher forms of life.

With a few exceptions, plants make their own food from water and air. To survive, they must act like pipelines, taking water out of the soil, delivering it to cells for use, and emptying whatever is left over into the air. The water, absorbed through the fine root hairs underground, travels upwards through bundles of long, microscopic tubes penetrating the stem and branches, and passes back to the atmosphere as transpiration through tiny leaf pores called stomata (which also serve as entrance and exit ports for the carbon dioxide and oxygen essential to photosynthesis and growth). One square inch of leaf may contain as many as 300,000 stomata, most of which are on the underside, and they release an astonishing amount of water. Although transpiration varies with conditions of temperature, humidity, light, wind, and soil moisture, it usually totals several hundred times the dry weight of the plant itself during a single growing season. During its lifetime, a crop of corn, for example, may release water sufficient to cover its entire field to a depth of 11 inches. And in one warm day a single birch tree can dispose of 50 to 70 gallons of water.

The mechanics of this remarkably capacious water-handling system are still not completely understood. The movement of water in certain plants—very tall trees, for example—poses one of the most intriguing puzzles of biology. What is known, however, testifies again to the distinctive characteristics of water.

Ground-water enters the root hairs of a plant by a special kind of diffusion called osmosis, a fundamental process that goes on in nearly all living tissues.

Through this process water molecules are able to cross living membranes which apparently will not admit water in the form of drops of liquid. This seeming paradox can be demonstrated with a piece of cellophane, which is a synthetic membrane quite similar to natural ones. Cellophane is watertight in the sense that a drop of water placed on its surface will not drip through; even when it is examined with an ordinary light microscope no pores can be seen. Yet water molecules do diffuse through cellophane despite its apparently smooth and continuous structure; as most housewives are aware, a slice of bread wrapped in cellophane will dry out—not so fast, of course, as if it had lain unwrapped, yet faster than if it had been wrapped in such impermeable material as aluminium foil.

Seeping through a membrane

A plant's membrane also seems smooth and continuous; a microscope reveals no pores. Yet somehow water crosses to enter the plant. This puzzling circumstance is resolved by a closer examination of the membrane. There are pores after all, but they are too small to be seen with an ordinary microscope. Like all substances, a membrane is composed of molecules. And the molecules, no matter how tightly they are packed together, have spaces between them. The spaces are large enough to offer easy passage to water molecules but are far too small to let water penetrate in packages as large as a drop. Thus, a drop *may* pass through the barrier—but only a few molecules of it at a time.

Diffusion, the force that plays a major part in pushing molecules through the pores of a plant membrane, arises from the random movements of the molecules, their continuous jiggling to and fro. They bounce against one another and fly apart, tending always to spread from a region where they are closely packed together to regions of lesser concentration. This action is the same one that diffuses dissolved molecules throughout a liquid—and is the reason a lump of sugar eventually sweetens a cup of coffee whether it is stirred or not.

The rate at which molecules slip through a plant's intermolecular pores depends on the size of both the molecules and the pores. Small molecules like those of water travel through the pores of living membranes at a fairly rapid rate. The larger molecules of substances that may be dissolved in water, such as minerals, travel through much more slowly. It is the difference in the rate of transmission that makes the membrane a kind of sieve; it can hold minerals on one side while letting water pass through.

This sieving action can build up a substantial pressure. The reason is that there are relatively more water molecules outside the plant than inside, where minerals are present in the liquid. The water molecules therefore flow from the region where they are proportionately more numerous, or more concentrated, to the region where their concentration is less. This osmotic pressure is great enough to raise a column of water as high as 66 feet through the trunk of a tree.

The mystery of the climbing water

Osmotic pressure is only one of the forces that drives water from roots through stem to the leaves of a plant. Aiding it is capillarity—the attraction between the molecules of water and those of other compounds that pulls liquid water upwards through the plant's microscopic tubes. Capillarity alone can raise water several feet in most plants. In addition, atmospheric pressure may push water upwards to fill low-pressure areas within a plant.

But none of these mechanisms can account for the enormous heights to which water is actually delivered in trees. In the Pacific North-West, for instance, there are Redwoods which tower almost 400 feet; since their roots may sink 50 feet into the ground, some of the water that reaches the tree top must be lifted a total of 450 feet. The pressure required for this task is more than 12 times as great as the pressure of the atmosphere at sea level.

No one knows for certain how this astonishing feat is accomplished. The best current theory explains it in terms of another outstanding characteristic of water: tensile strength, or resistance to being pulled apart. Hydrogen bonds link the molecules in liquid water so tightly that a column of water is as strong in some ways as a tough chain. Laboratory experiments have demonstrated that very pure water, enclosed in a slender, airtight tube, can withstand a pull of 5,000 pounds per square inch—a tensile strength close to that of some metals. The tensile strength of plant sap is less; it amounts to some 3,000 pounds per square inch. Still this is enough to enable a slender column of sap, enclosed in one of the fine fibrous tubes of a tree, to be lifted several thousand feet—much higher than the height of any tree.

But water's great tensile strength does not become a factor in the process of climbing a tree unless some kind of force is exerted on the column. This is supplied by transpiration. When water transpires from the leaves, it lowers the concentration in the cell walls. The cell walls replace this lost moisture by pulling in water molecules from the liquid in the shoot. This transfer of water molecules puts the tree's columns of water under tension, as if they were being grabbed at the top and

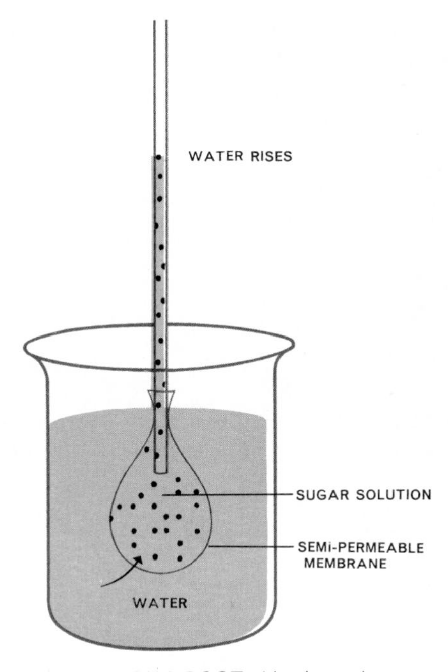

AN ARTIFICIAL ROOT, this glass tube attached to a cellophane sac brings water upwards as a plant does. The sac contains a sugar solution, and the cellophane lets water but not sugar pass through it. Because the concentration of water is greater outside the sac, water enters by the process of osmosis. Thus the solution rises in the tube.

hauled upwards. Since these columns are continuous from leaves to roots, the pulling at the top raises water from the bottom, a molecule at a time.

There seem to be obvious holes in the theory. What happens if the slender column of water breaks? This must disrupt the whole continuous water-raising process. It is difficult to see how such breaks can be avoided as trees sway in a high wind; certainly they cannot be avoided when whole branches are lopped off. Yet neither wind nor cutting wounds seem seriously to affect the rise of water. In certain respects, the process remains an enigma.

A multipurpose fluid

No such mystery surrounds the circulation of water in animals. They have mechanical pumps—hearts—to assist capillarity and osmosis in supplying water to body parts. With this added complexity goes far greater complexity of water use. In animals as in plants, water serves as the common carrier, transporting food and waste, oxygen and carbon dioxide, and it plays a critical role in the digestion of food. In animals it also serves to lubricate the joints, lest they creak, and the soft tissues, lest they stick. Its cooling action keeps the heat of metabolism from becoming unbearable. Further, all these demands require involved systems for controlling the water. Its quantity and concentration must be regulated precisely—either too much or too little may quickly cause death.

The human body gets its water from several sources. Only about 47 per cent is supplied in the most obvious way, by drinking. As much as 14 per cent of the daily requirement is manufactured by the body itself as a by-product of the chemical process of cellular respiration. Another 39 per cent or so comes from what we think of as "solid" food. Most food-stuffs—the living cells of vegetables and animals raised to be eaten—contain at least as much water as the cells of human beings; only fats, such as butter, are largely without water content. A tomato, for example, is 94 per cent water. Meats are 50 to 70 per cent water, and bread contains about 35 per cent.

Water is involved in the most fundamental process of the human body. Acting on food with the help of chemical accelerators called enzymes, it breaks up the great molecules of carbohydrates into simple molecular groups—chiefly the sugar glucose—that are small enough to be absorbed through cell membranes. There these molecules can combine with oxygen, also transported into the cell in water solution, and become metabolized: the food is oxidized, or "burned", to produce energy for the body. The products of this combustion are organic compounds—such as starch, which can be stored, heat, which must be distributed

THE SATURATED BODY of a man is 65 per cent water. The liquid permeates all human tissue, fills cellular gaps and bony hollows, and flows through 60,000 miles of arteries and veins. Water in the cells makes up 41 per cent of the body's weight, the blood plasma provides 4 per cent and the fluid occupying empty cavities, such as the intestines or eyeballs, comprises 5 per cent. This distribution is not static: water knows no anatomical boundaries and passes constantly through membranes from one compartment of the body to another.

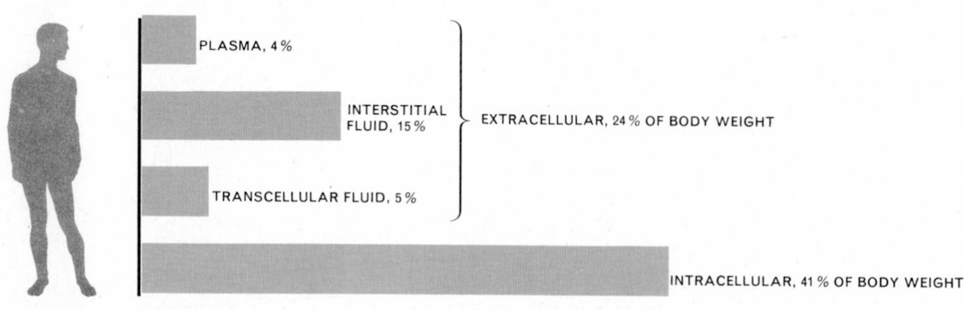

at once, and carbon dioxide, which is carried to the lungs. Another product of this metabolic "burning" is additional water, which remains in the body and joins the other water taken in from outside.

The heat of the body's metabolic fires is far greater than might be supposed. When called on it can perform astonishing feats—such as enabling the primitive Indians of Tierra del Fuego to survive, without clothes and unshivering, in their bitter, near-Arctic climate.

Water helps to control this heat. It absorbs large quantities of metabolic heat with comparatively little increase in temperature; its rapid circulation throughout the body via the blood-stream enables it to carry excess heat to the surface of the body for quick release to the surrounding air. In this sense it works exactly like the coolant in any liquid-cooled engine. And a related property, water's high latent heat of vaporization, further helps to protect the body from high temperatures. Water in the form of perspiration disposes of almost three times as much heat in the process of evaporation as the same weight of alcohol. In addition, water protects the internal chemical processes of the body from violent fluctuations in pressure, acidity and chemical composition.

The body's water-control centre

While water is itself the great stabilizer of bodily processes, its own balance must be regulated—not only in quantity but also in the concentration of dissolved materials. The balance of water within the body needs to be very precise; a variation of no more than 1 or 2 per cent from the normal immediately makes itself felt as thirst or pain. The master control centre is the hypothalamus, a small section in the centre of the brain just above the spinal cord. The hypothalamus governs processes that must be responded to automatically without any delay for conscious decisions: heart action, sleeping and waking, appetite, sex, digestion and thirst. It maintains water balance by secreting a hormone that regulates the kidneys and also stimulates nerves at the back of the throat. True thirst is sensed mainly there—even a man dying of lack of water might feel no thirst if his throat could be kept moist.

Either too much or too little water can be disastrous. When a man loses only 5 per cent of his normal body water, his skin will shrink, his mouth and tongue will go dry, and he may experience hallucinations; a loss of 15 per cent is usually fatal. Too much water causes nausea and weakness, and enforced drinking—the water "cure" inflicted by some savages on their enemies—leads successively to mental confusion, disorientation, tremors, convulsions, coma and death.

Besides controlling the total amount of water, the body must carefully meter the materials dissolved in it. Too great a loss of salt through heavy perspiration, for example, brings on heat cramps. The muscle cells react to the loss of salt by contracting into hard and painful knots. Too much salt—from drinking sea-water, for example—causes a tortured death as the cells become dried out and shrivelled.

Water leaves the body by several routes. About 15 per cent is exhaled in the breath, and perspiration evaporates another 20 per cent, although this last figure may jump to 33 per cent in hot weather. The rest is released by direct excretion. While these proportions may vary, the combined rate of disposal is always held within narrow limits. Excretion rarely falls below the minimum of about three and a half pints per day, no matter how dehydrated one may be. To survive, a human being must always balance this limited loss by acquiring close to his average four or five pints of water every day, neither much more nor much less. He cannot live in water, but neither can he live far from it.

Adapting to arid life

Some animals and many plants are not so restricted. They can flourish where water seems totally absent. They do require water, of course, but unusual adaptations enable them to get along with small amounts, to acquire it from hidden sources, and to survive long periods of total drought. Desert animals conserve water by foraging at night, when lower temperatures make water losses far less than they would be during the day. They keep out of the sun as much as they can, often living underground. And many of them, like the armadillo and the desert-dwelling lizards, have developed hides that are virtually impervious to water and protect them from water loss. By far the most abundant desert-dwelling mammals are the varieties of small rodents. Though they live in all the world's deserts, probably the greatest numbers exist in the vast desert complex that stretches from the west African coast, across the Sahara, to Arabia, through Asia and into China. Many of these rodents look much the same the world over, and subsist on dry seeds and plants that contain only slight amounts of "free water". They gain the rest that they need by combining the oxygen in the air with hydrogen from the seeds. While conservation of water and a diet of dry food are the adaptations for survival of small desert mammals, other desert animals, the predators, survive by preying upon these creatures. The major killers are the big snakes—pythons and boas—that eat everything from rodents and rabbits to small antelopes and kangaroos. The same holds true for another group of desert predators, the carnivores—including foxes and various kinds of cats.

Still more varied are the habits of plants. Those which must cope with occasional droughts can simply shut off or drastically reduce transpiration. The guard cells of the leaf stomata are designed so that they hold the pores open only when the cells are turgid with water; when the plants wilt, as they do when water becomes deficient, the pores close.

Plants of the driest deserts carry this process further; their stomata normally open only at night. Plants like ocotillo accomplish the same end by dropping their leaves during time of drought and growing new foliage following a rain. Cacti, whose leaves have been reduced to spines, have a thick, waxy cuticle which prevents the escape of water. The barrel cactus is well known for its ability to absorb and conserve large amounts of water, and many tales are told of how it has saved the lives of travellers dying of thirst in America's Western deserts. After a rain, its thousands of roots take in moisture from the soil. This moisture is then carried up into the plant, whose cylindrical body swells to barrel-like proportions as it makes room for its water supply and shrinks again as the supply is used up. Contrary to popular belief, however, drinking water cannot be obtained from the barrel cactus simply by cutting off its top and draining off its liquid contents. The inside is a white pulpy mass which must be crushed in order to extract its bitter but potable juice.

Another group of desert plants, the ephemerals, has adapted to take prompt advantage of infrequent desert rain. The seeds of these plants are remarkably long-lived, yet quick to germinate in the presence of the slightest moisture. Ephemerals mature with amazing rapidity, completing their entire life cycle within a few weeks. These are the plants which spread a carpet of colour across the desert after a single spring shower, then almost as quickly disappear.

Death in the desert

For man, the desert remains a hostile environment, as inhospitable as space or the open sea. His inability to limit his body's consumption of water or to reduce the amount it loses—his total dependence on a regular intake of water—never confronts him more clearly than when he ventures into arid land. In 1965 an Egyptian desert patrol on routine duty came across the bodies of five travellers lying lifeless beneath the searing sun. The tragedy was unique only in the detailed record the dead had left behind. From notebooks and from photographs—one taken only hours before their death—it was possible to reconstruct a fairly accurate record of what had happened to them.

They were Germans living in Egypt, who had set out from Cairo on the first Saturday in June in two Volkswagens, a sedan and an estate car, for a short visit to the Roman temple ruins at the Siwa oasis 300 miles across the Libyan desert. They had kept to the coast road until they reached El Alamein in the afternoon, and had then turned south across the trackless desert. Some time on Sunday, first the sedan, then the estate car, broke down in the sand. At that time they had two gallons of water and five large cans of mango juice between them.

If they had used every possible trick to reduce perspiration—had kept themselves covered, had improvised some shade and had remained quietly by the cars—they might have survived until found. But foolishly, perhaps from delirium in the 60° C. heat, they changed into bathing suits and set off to find help. In less than two days they were dead, their bodies totally drained of moisture. By ignoring the fragile link of water that sustains all life, they had made disaster inevitable.

The Indispensable Fluid

An adequate water supply is literally a matter of life or death, not only for human beings but for every form of animal and plant life, from the lowliest amoeba to the tallest redwood tree. A man would soon die if he lost as little as 12 per cent of his body's water, and almost every organism is heavily dependent on water for more than 50 per cent of its body weight. Water dissolves and distributes such necessities of life as carbon dioxide, oxygen and salts. In the human body water is essential for blood circulation, waste removal and even muscle movements: without it, a man could not so much as bat an eyelash.

Every organism must constantly replenish water lost through excretion and evaporation, and each has evolved an effective means of satisfying its need. This endless thirst is a legacy of the sea, in which all life began. Biochemists believe that the concentration of salt in human protoplasm —0.9 per cent—is the same as that of the sea 3,000 million years ago, when the first living organisms took to the land. Thus, in a figurative sense, man still carries within him the primordial waters from which his ancestors emerged.

A THIRSTY THICKET

The tangled plants of the forest, their distinctive leaves glistening in the rain, are equipped by nature to maintain a delicate balance between too much and too little water. Their efficient root systems absorb more water than the plants retain. Some is stored for later use and the rest is eliminated by the leaves—either transpired as vapour or forced out in the form of dew-like droplets.

Drawing Moisture from Sea and Soil

Plants, like cities, often find their need for water far greater than the readily available supply. And like cities, they tend to develop increasingly elaborate supply systems as water becomes harder to find. For some plants, like the aquatic algae on the left below, the system is quite simple. They absorb water—which makes up 95 per cent of their substance—by direct contact, and would quickly perish if removed from their water-filled environment. The semi-aquatic marsh plant (*centre*) merely extends its body an inch or two into the damp ground for all its water.

By contrast, the land plant has evolved a root system that can absorb moisture from as far as 30 feet underground. A single rye plant may have 14,000 million root hairs, with a root network totalling 380 miles. In a single growing season, a plant may soak up 20 times its dry weight in water.

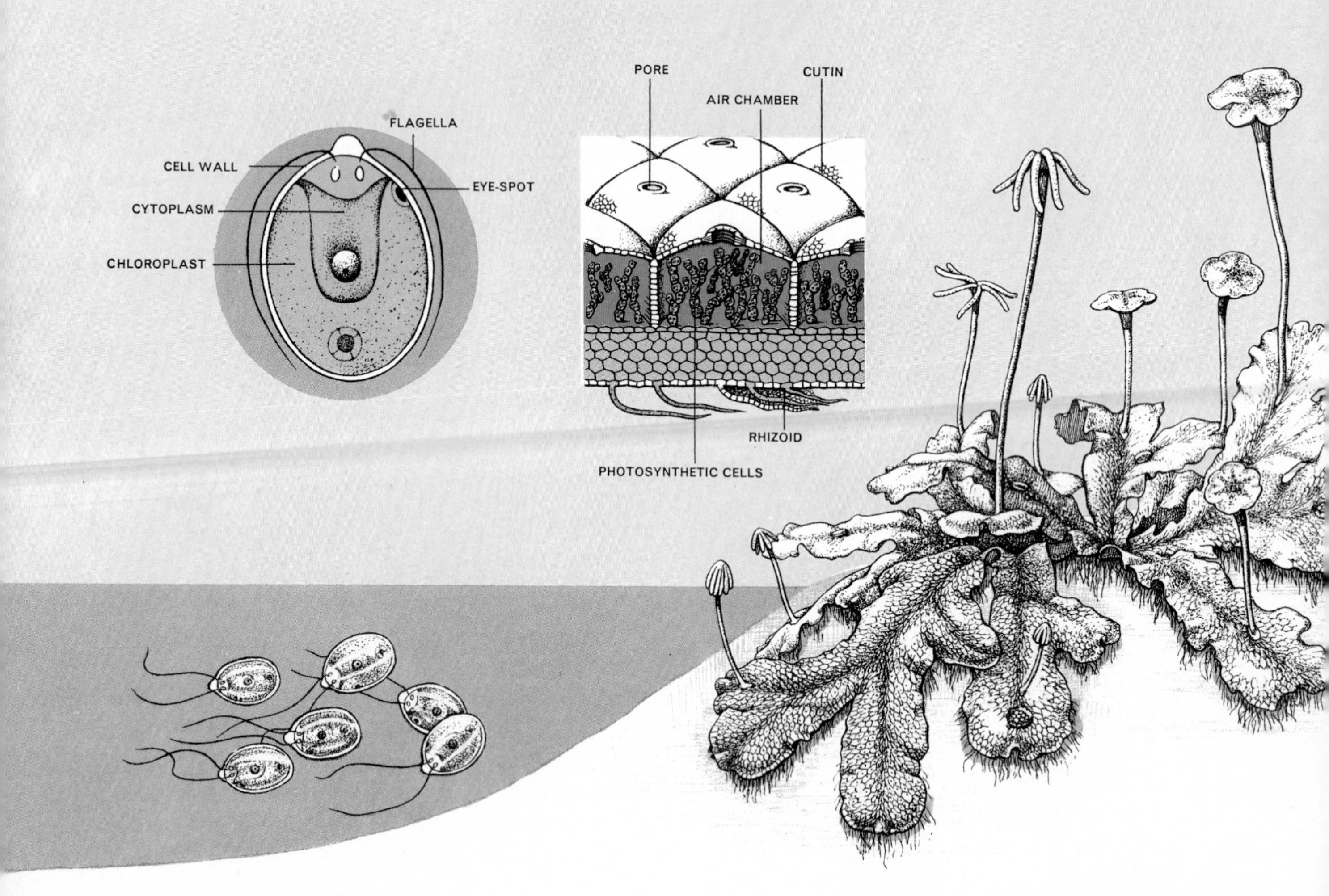

THE SIMPLEST SYSTEM
The single-celled algae *Chlamydomonas*, which float by the millions in green, scum-like clusters, need no roots since water is filtered directly through their cell walls. Food is manufactured by a photosynthetic process in the chloroplast, then stored in the cytoplasm. The eye-spot dictates movements by the flagella towards light.

BETWEEN LAND AND WATER
The *Marchantia*, a moss-like liverwort without roots, leaves or stem, grows on water-saturated soil. The pores of the marsh plant admit air to tiny chambers containing water drawn up by root-like rhizoids. Chlorophyll cells then produce food photosynthetically, while the waxy cutin surface prevents excessive evaporation.

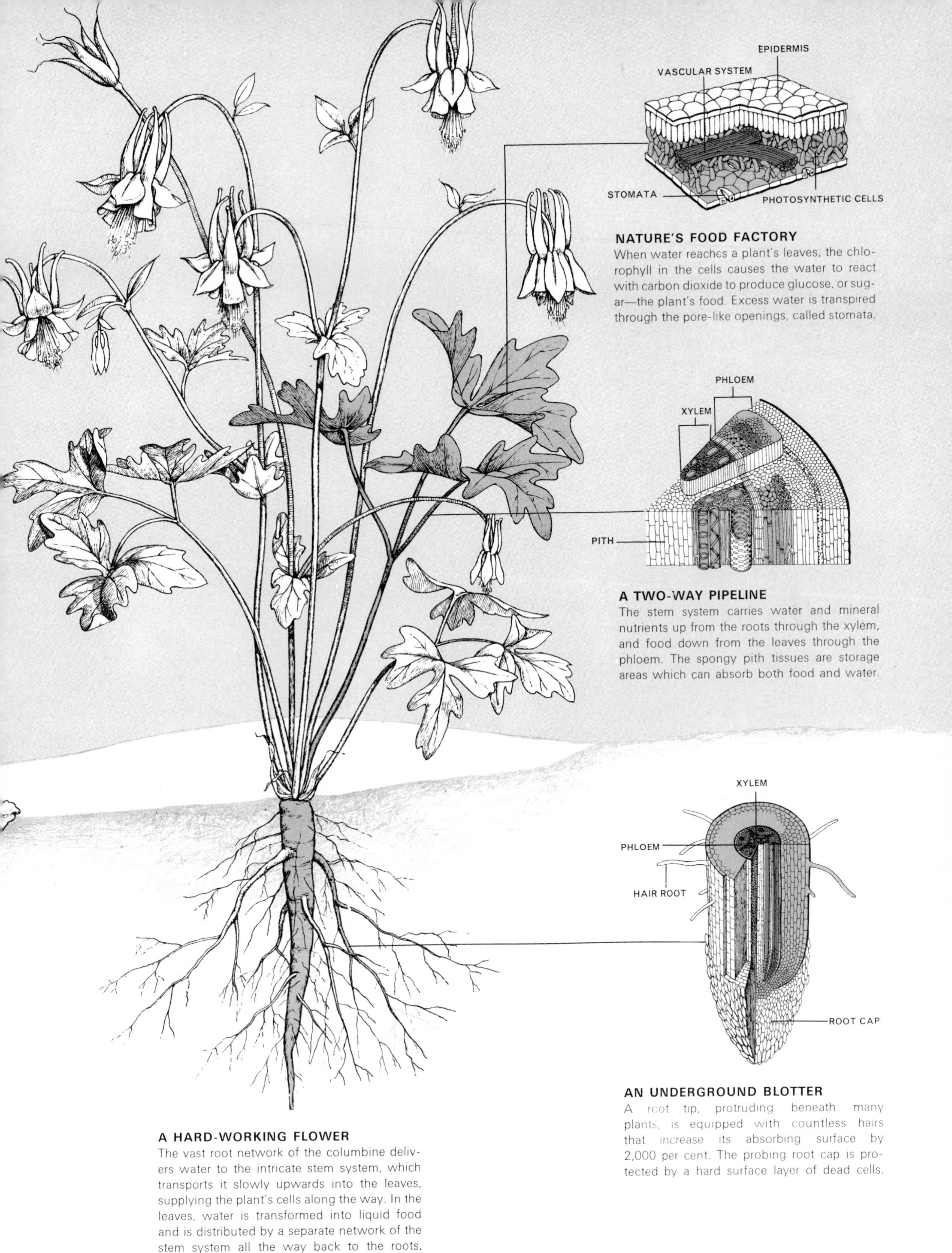

NATURE'S FOOD FACTORY

When water reaches a plant's leaves, the chlorophyll in the cells causes the water to react with carbon dioxide to produce glucose, or sugar—the plant's food. Excess water is transpired through the pore-like openings, called stomata.

A TWO-WAY PIPELINE

The stem system carries water and mineral nutrients up from the roots through the xylem, and food down from the leaves through the phloem. The spongy pith tissues are storage areas which can absorb both food and water.

AN UNDERGROUND BLOTTER

A root tip, protruding beneath many plants, is equipped with countless hairs that increase its absorbing surface by 2,000 per cent. The probing root cap is protected by a hard surface layer of dead cells.

A HARD-WORKING FLOWER

The vast root network of the columbine delivers water to the intricate stem system, which transports it slowly upwards into the leaves, supplying the plant's cells along the way. In the leaves, water is transformed into liquid food and is distributed by a separate network of the stem system all the way back to the roots.

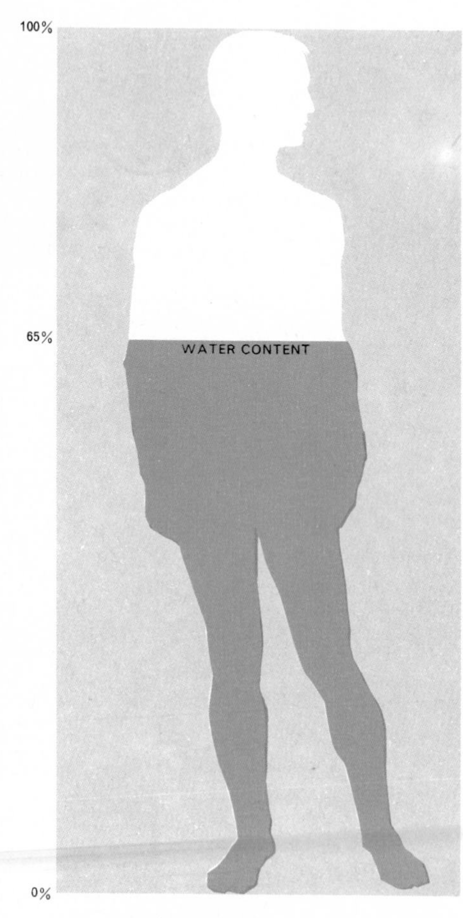

THE WATERY HUMAN

The amount of water in the human body, averaging 65 per cent, varies considerably from person to person and even from one part of the body to another (*right*). A lean man may have as much as 70 per cent of his weight in the form of body water, while a woman, because of her larger proportion of water-poor fatty tissues, may be only 52 per cent water. The lowering of the water content in the blood is what triggers the hypothalamus, the brain's thirst centre, to send out its familiar demand for a drink.

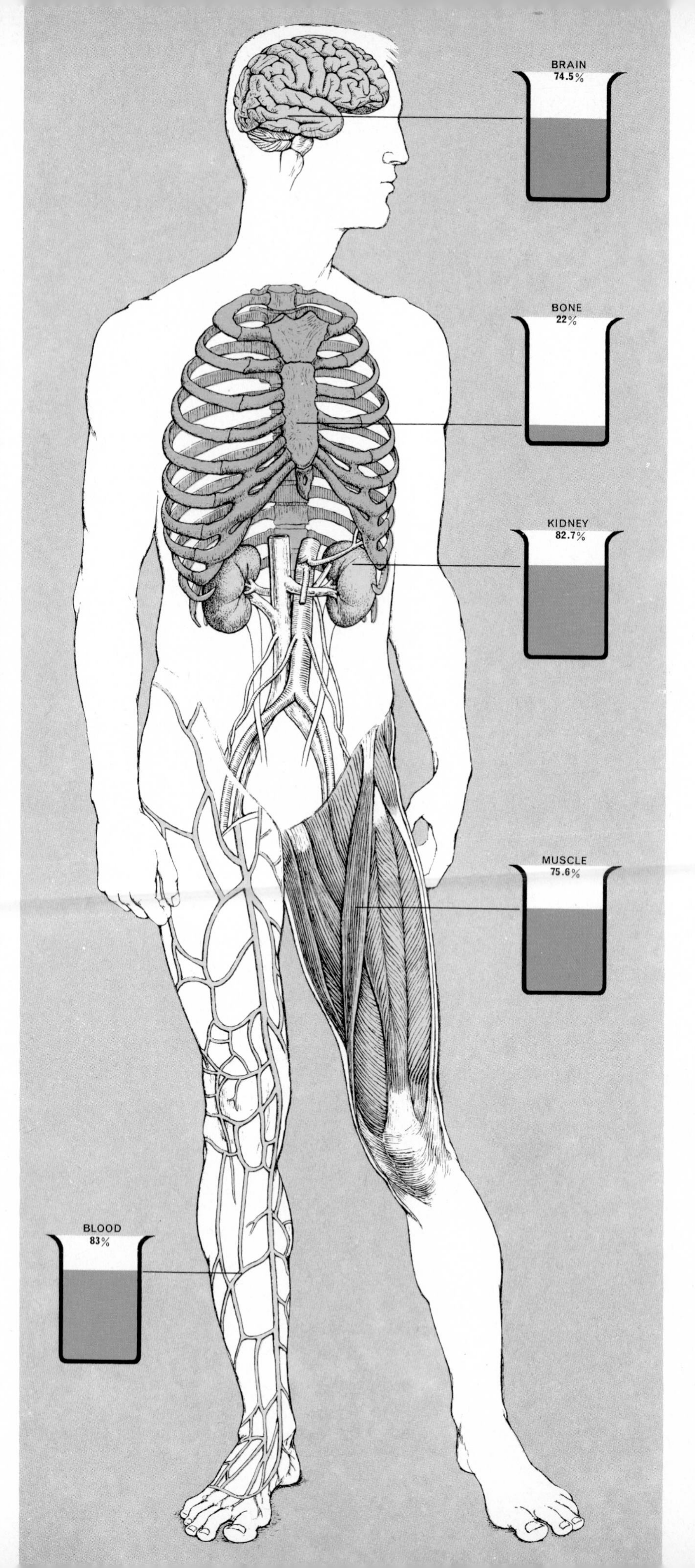

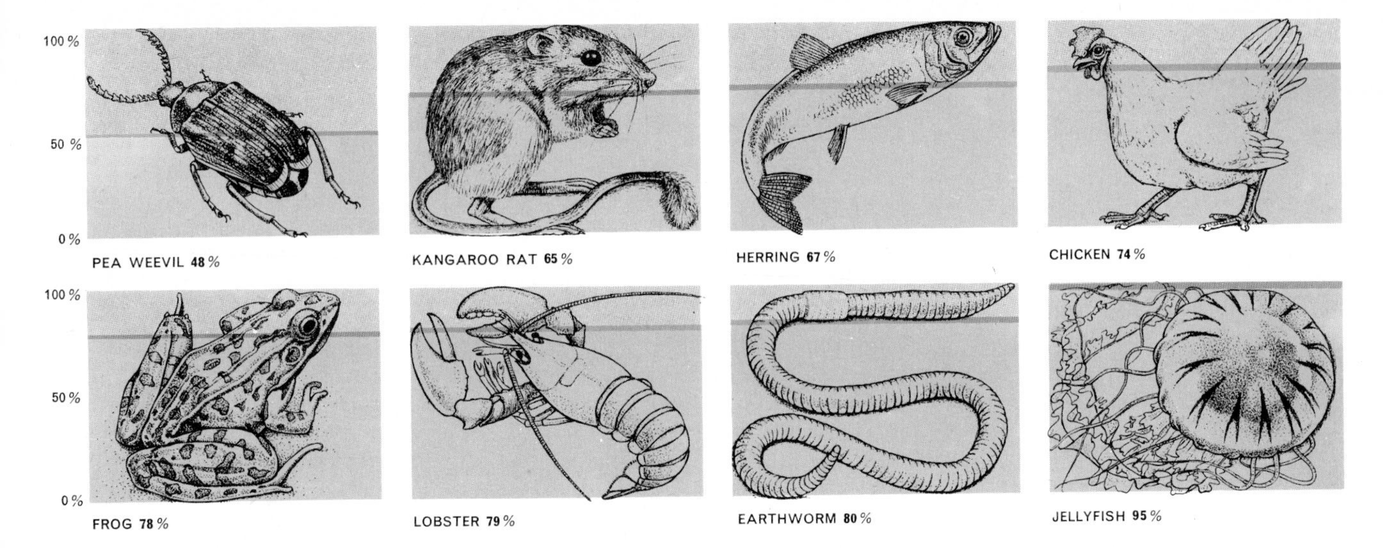

THE THIRSTY ANIMAL KINGDOM

Animals, unlike plants, must maintain fairly rigid percentages of water in their bodies in order to live. Most, however, have adapted their physiology to match the water levels of their environment: the desert-dwelling kangaroo rat gets along on an absolute minimum of water, and the pea weevil needs very little—but the jellyfish must remain immersed. Between these extremes are some surprises. Herring have about the same water proportion as mammals. The earthworm actually contains more water than either the aquatic lobster or amphibious frog.

A Universal Craving for Water

The average man has approximately 40 quarts (about 100 pounds) of water in his body and every day he must replace a little more than two quarts of it. Drinking returns about one quart and the water in food brings in nearly another quart; about half a pint is produced by the metabolizing of "dry" food. Like all mammals, man uses water throughout his body, from 2 per cent in tooth enamel to 83 per cent in his blood. He may live without food for more than two months but would probably die without water in less than a week. Some mammals, however, are gifted with unusual ability to go without water. The donkey can survive in a desert for four days; in the process it may lose 30 per cent of its body weight in water—doubling the amount that would fatally dehydrate a human. But while man replenishes his body water in short doses, both by drinking and by eating watery foods (*below*), the donkey is one of the world's fastest, most avid drinkers. It can down five gallons of water in two minutes.

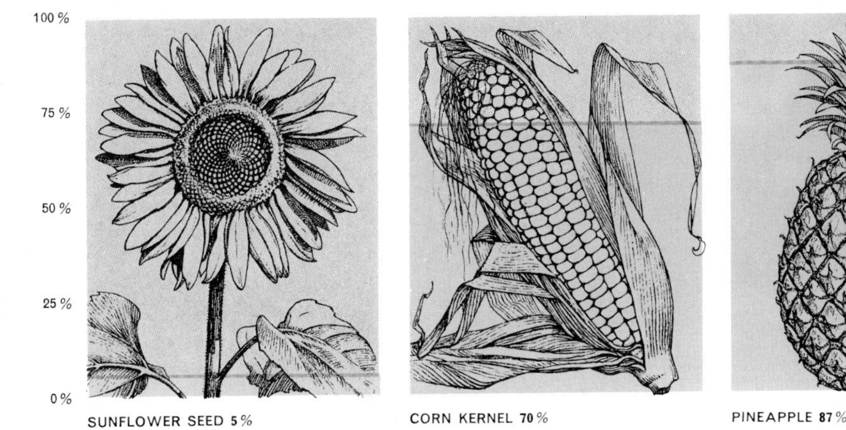

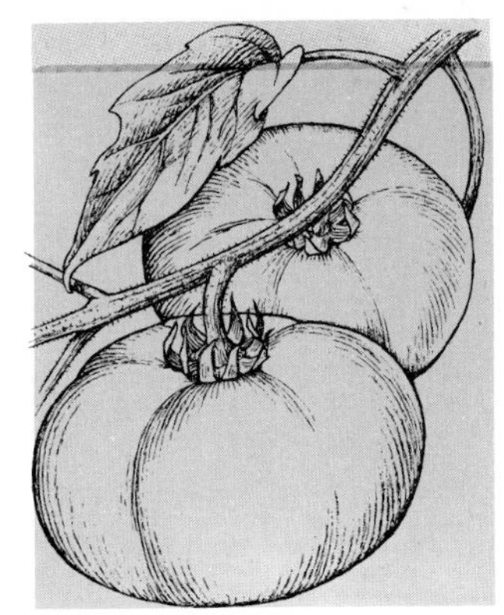

FOOD FOR DRINKING

Fruit and vegetables, which fill much of man's water needs, tend to increase their percentages of water as they ripen. Thus an apple seed, only 10 per cent water, will eventually produce fruit that is 80 per cent water. A ripe pineapple or tomato is virtually saturated with water, while corn kernels are more moist than the inedible cob on which they grow. Even the driest food that man can eat—baked sunflower seeds—is 5 per cent water. The wettest is the aptly named watermelon, which ripens into a summer thirst-quencher that is 97 per cent water

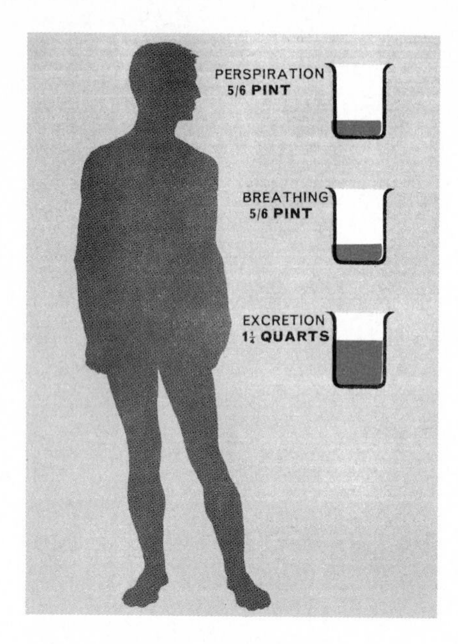

THE OUTFLOW OF WATER
Most of the body's water loss is through kidney waste fluid, or urine, which is roughly 95 per cent water. But ordinary breathing and perspiration dispose of $1\frac{2}{3}$ pints of water per day.

The Body's Busiest Substance

There is no stagnant water in the body. All the water molecules present in any part of the body at any given moment are somewhere else seconds later, and have been replaced by new molecules. Much of this water is re-circulated and used over and over again, but a little more than two quarts a day—an amount equal to the daily intake—is permanently removed, or excreted, in various ways. There is a small but steady outflow through the tear glands, which produce a salty secretion that lubricates and cleans the eyes. The sweat glands use up $\frac{5}{6}$ of a pint of water each day in cooling the skin's surface by evaporation. The normal breathing process draws off another $\frac{5}{6}$ of a pint as exhaled air carries moisture out of the lungs. But nowhere does the body's water perform a more vital function than in the kidneys, where it serves as the medium which purges wastes from the blood-stream. Fifteen times an hour, all the blood in the body passes through the two kidneys. A total of about 200 gallons of blood is "washed" each day; from this amount two quarts of waste are removed as urine. The rest is absorbed back into the blood-stream. The kidneys are so efficient that even if one is incapacitated the other can continue cleaning the entire blood supply by itself. If both kidneys fail, however, a condition known as uraemia results: salts and other wastes pollute the blood. A man cannot live more than three weeks with uncleansed blood.

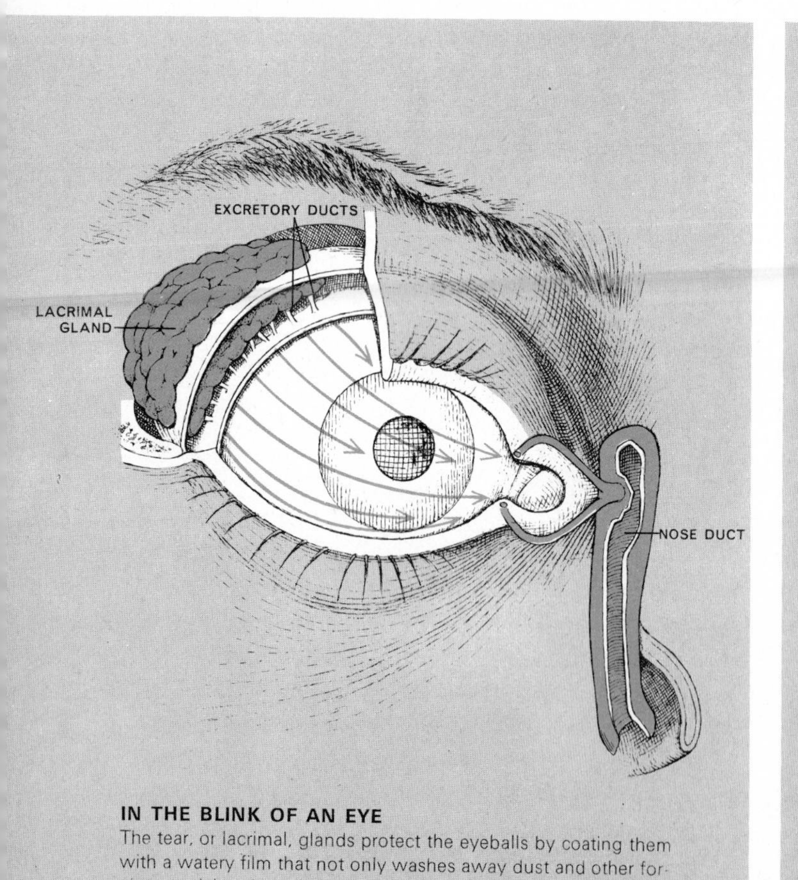

IN THE BLINK OF AN EYE
The tear, or lacrimal, glands protect the eyeballs by coating them with a watery film that not only washes away dust and other foreign particles, but also lubricates the surface for the blinking eyelids. Tiny excretory ducts carry the liquid to the upper lids, which sweep it over the eyes 25 times every minute. Eventually the tears are ducted down into the nose, where they evaporate.

TWO MILLION WATER COOLERS
The body's two million sweat glands, which work unnoticed at normal temperatures, step up their activity whenever the body becomes overheated. Obeying a signal flashed from the brain, the glands excrete sweat—which is 99 per cent water, with fractions of salt and urea. The heat of the blood, brought close to the skin by capillaries, evaporates the sweat—a process which cools the body.

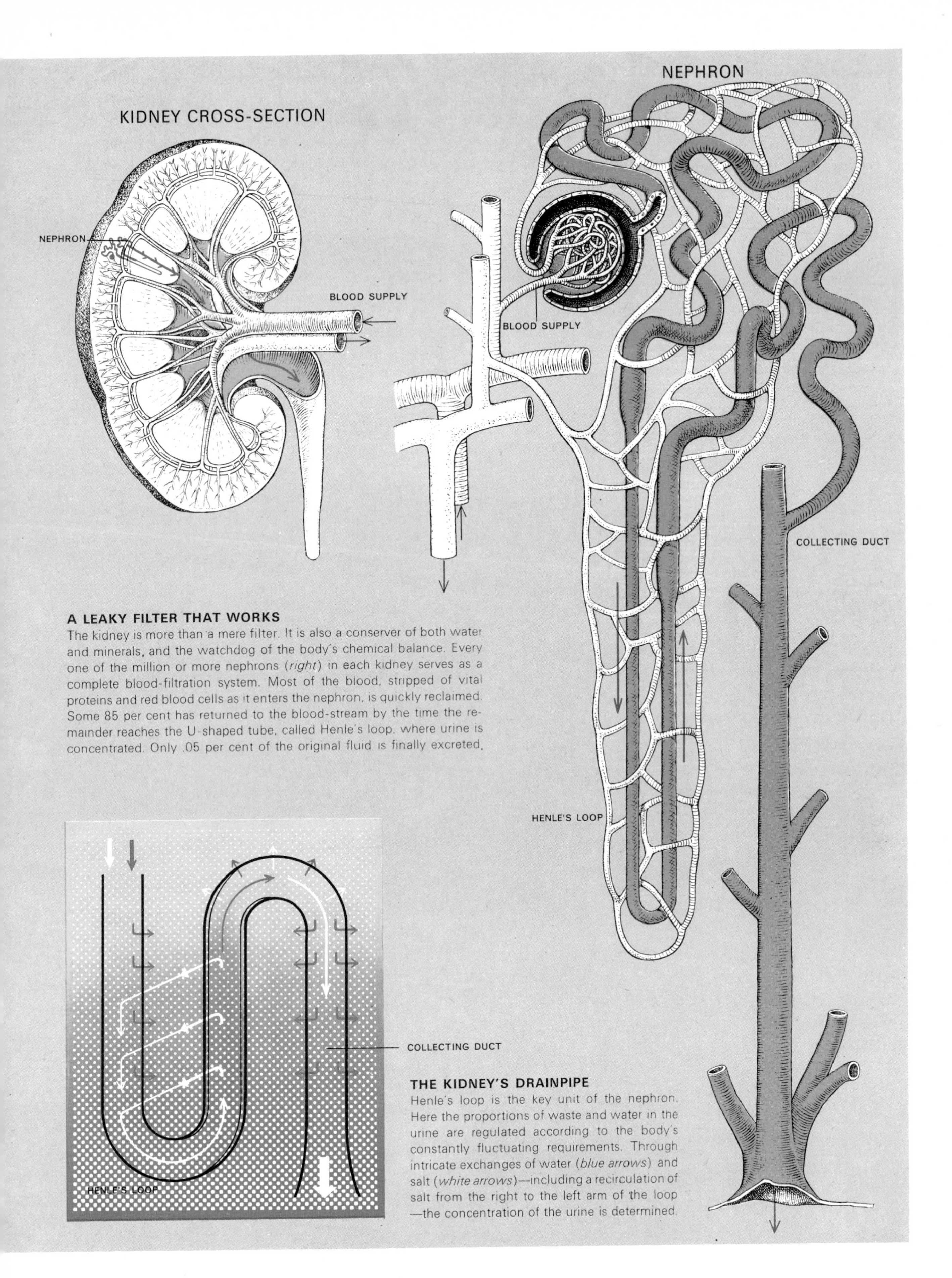

A LEAKY FILTER THAT WORKS

The kidney is more than a mere filter. It is also a conserver of both water and minerals, and the watchdog of the body's chemical balance. Every one of the million or more nephrons (*right*) in each kidney serves as a complete blood-filtration system. Most of the blood, stripped of vital proteins and red blood cells as it enters the nephron, is quickly reclaimed. Some 85 per cent has returned to the blood-stream by the time the remainder reaches the U-shaped tube, called Henle's loop, where urine is concentrated. Only .05 per cent of the original fluid is finally excreted.

THE KIDNEY'S DRAINPIPE

Henle's loop is the key unit of the nephron. Here the proportions of waste and water in the urine are regulated according to the body's constantly fluctuating requirements. Through intricate exchanges of water (*blue arrows*) and salt (*white arrows*)—including a recirculation of salt from the right to the left arm of the loop —the concentration of the urine is determined.

Flushing Out the Body's Salt

All organisms keep the amount of salt in their bodies in balance, using water to remove excessive amounts of the substance. (No animal can tolerate a body-salt concentration of more than 0.9 per cent.) Human kidneys, incapable of concentrating more than 2.2 per cent salt in urine, cannot cope with sea-water, which is 3.5 per cent salt; if a man drank enough sea-water, his body would dehydrate itself trying to flush out the excess. The horse, with even less efficient kidneys, cannot drink water from certain brackish streams that is perfectly fit for human consumption. But some animals can cope with heavy doses of salt. Two of these, the camel and kangaroo rat, live in the desert, where water is scarce. The camel, even though it can survive a 40 per cent loss of its body weight in water, needs every possible drop to cool its body under the broiling sun. The nocturnal kangaroo rat, which never drinks at all, metabolizes about two ounces of water every five weeks from its diet of dry seeds. It loses only a drop or two in ridding itself of unwanted salt. The whale, a mammalian sea dweller, has kidneys so efficient that it can drink sea-water without harm. Most marine birds and reptiles, however, are equipped with special glands designed exclusively for salt removal. Using these glands, a thirsty gull can drink up to one-tenth of its weight in sea-water—which would be equivalent to $1\frac{3}{4}$ gallons in man—and excrete all excess salt in about three hours.

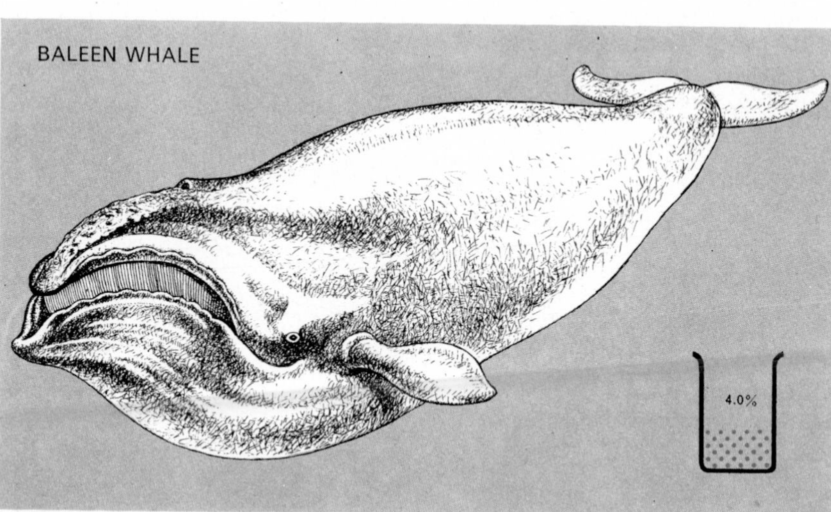

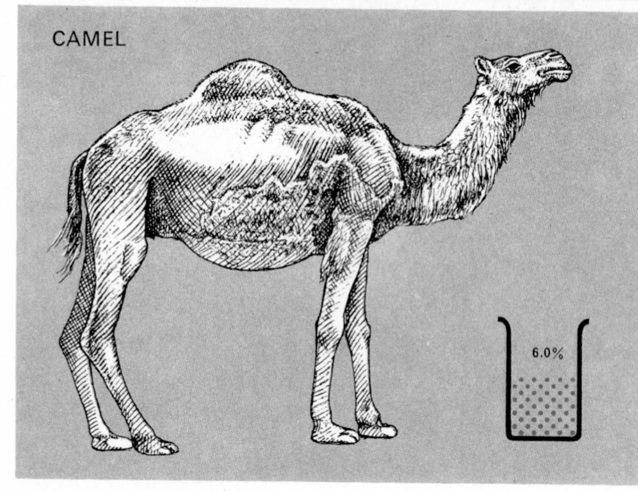

THE ENVIRONMENTAL FACTOR

The amount of salt an animal can concentrate in its urine is directly related to its need for water. Creatures such as the camel and kangaroo rat, which live where water is scarce, cannot afford to use much of it for flushing; as a consequence, the amount of their urine is slight but the concentration of salt in it is high. The kidneys of the horse, an animal which consumes large quantities of water and excretes freely, produce a very low percentage of salt. The whale, while it can drink sea-water, gets most of its salt and water from the marine life on which it feeds.

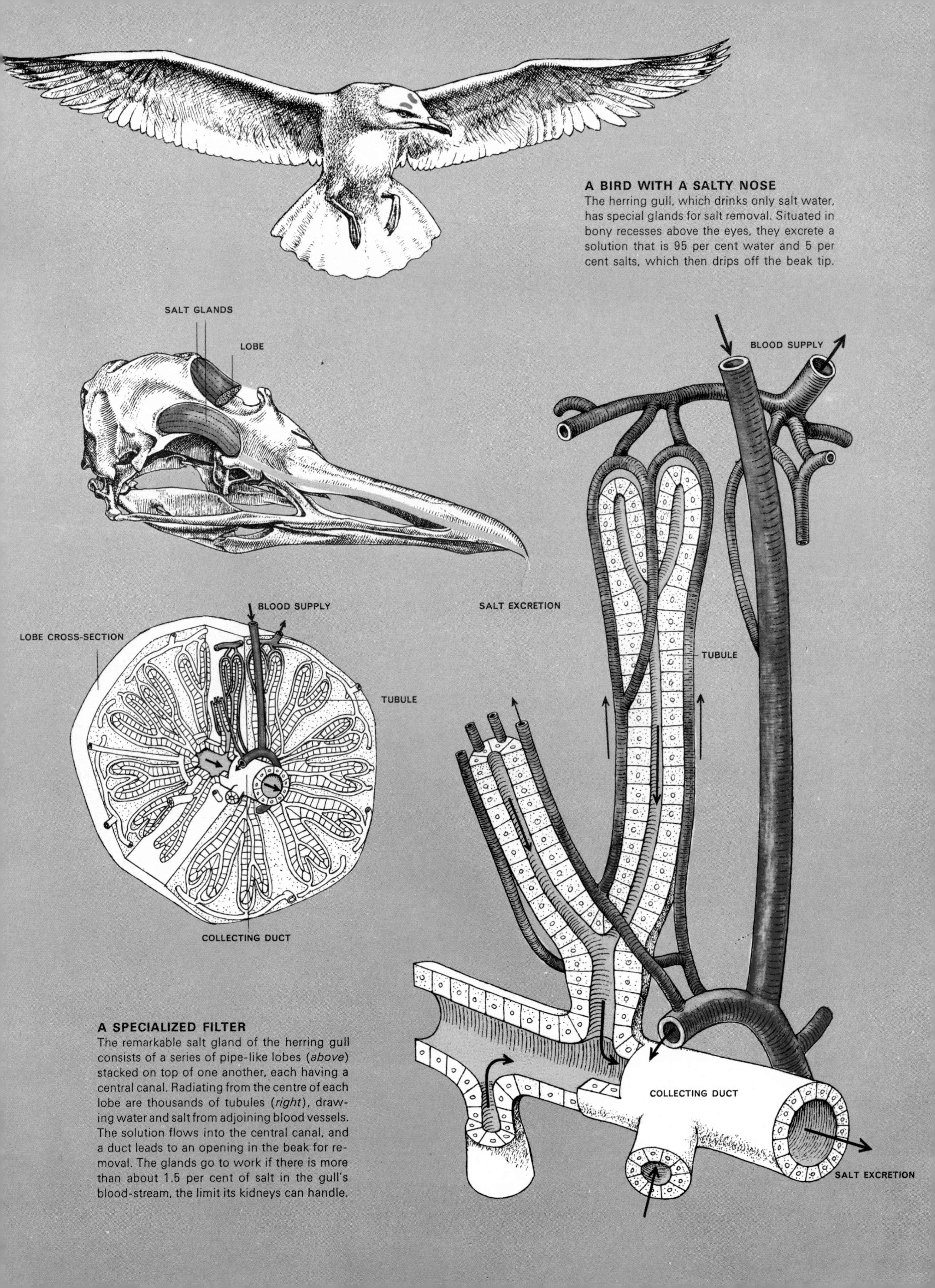

A BIRD WITH A SALTY NOSE
The herring gull, which drinks only salt water, has special glands for salt removal. Situated in bony recesses above the eyes, they excrete a solution that is 95 per cent water and 5 per cent salts, which then drips off the beak tip.

A SPECIALIZED FILTER
The remarkable salt gland of the herring gull consists of a series of pipe-like lobes (*above*) stacked on top of one another, each having a central canal. Radiating from the centre of each lobe are thousands of tubules (*right*), drawing water and salt from adjoining blood vessels. The solution flows into the central canal, and a duct leads to an opening in the beak for removal. The glands go to work if there is more than about 1.5 per cent of salt in the gull's blood-stream, the limit its kidneys can handle.

6

Wellsprings of Civilization

LIFE-GIVING MONSOON RAINS FALL ON THE TERRACED RICE PADDIES OF SOUTH-EASTERN NEPAL, HIGH IN THE HIMALAYA MOUNTAINS. IN THE BACKGROUND IS THE RIVER KOSI.

TODAY SAND SWIRLS around the eroded columns and crumbling walls of Leptis Magna, east of Tripoli on the coast of Libya. Beyond the ruins lies wasteland—all that remains of one of ancient Rome's most important supply ports. Two thousand years ago, Leptis Magna was a busy market and shipping centre, with elegant homes and public buildings. Water, provided by masterful engineers, helped to give life to the thriving city.

Leptis Magna's water supply, however, failed to survive the city's decline. Vandals and Berbers sacked the port in the fifth and sixth centuries, and the apathetic citizens allowed the harbour to fill with silt. Aqueducts, reservoirs, baths and fountains gradually decayed. Its waterworks gone, Leptis Magna became a forgotten city.

Grander societies than that of Leptis Magna have waxed and waned with the successes and failures of their water engineers. Without access to and some degree of control over water, human life at its simplest and its most complex would be impossible. The record of man's response to that fact constitutes much of the history of civilization.

From the beginning, water has furnished man with a source of food and a highway to travel upon. The first civilizations arose where water was a dominant element in the environment, a challenge to man's ingenuity. The Egyptians invented the 365-day calendar in response to the Nile's annual flooding. The Babylonians, among the most famous lawmakers of antiquity, devised edicts regulating water usage. Water inspired the Chinese to build a 1,000-mile canal, a complex system that, after nearly 2,500 years, is still partly in use and still commands the awe of engineers. But the ancients never found complete solutions to their water problems. The Hwang Ho, or Yellow River, is also known as "China's Sorrow"—it is so erratic and dangerous that in a single flood it has caused a million deaths. Floods harassed the great civilization of the Indus River valley, and inadequate drainage ruined much of its land. Today water dominates man as it always has. Its presence continues to govern the locations of his homes and cities; its tempestuous variability can kill him or his herds or his crops; its routes link him to his fellows; its immense value may add to already dangerous political frictions—for example, between the Arab States and Israel, and India and Pakistan in our own time.

The first attempts to master water-supply problems began during the Neolithic, or New Stone Age, when men learned to plant crops and settled the valleys of at least four great and widely separated river systems—the Nile of Egypt, the Tigris-Euphrates of Mesopotamia, the Indus of northern India and the Hwang Ho, or Yellow River, of China. Each gave birth to a mighty civilization.

"Egypt", said Herodotus, "is the gift of the Nile", and the statement is as true today as it was when the Greek historian uttered it 2,400 years ago. In late June, with clockwork regularity, the lower Nile, swollen by the tropical rains and melting mountain snows of its upper reaches, begins to rise. By late September, the whole of its flood-plain is a lake of turbid water. Then, as the waters slowly recede, shrinking back into the main channel by late October, they spread a rich residue of silt across the plain. Towards the end of the fourth millennium B.C., the Egyptians had turned their primitive hydraulic-engineering skills to making the most of the river's generally benign floods; simple canals, dikes and reservoirs helped them to husband water and increase their crops.

Menes, legendary founder of the first dynasty of kings, was famous for the vast hydraulic works he built in the area of Memphis, his capital, around 3100 B.C. Under later pharaohs, Menes' systems were extended until Egyptian waterworks, mainly canals for irrigation and swamp drainage, became a marvel of the early world.

Not all of the Egyptians' projects succeeded. The oldest known dam was built between 2700 and 2500 B.C. across a normally dry wadi, or stream bed, a few miles below Helwan. Its bulk was truly impressive—370 feet across the top, nearly 270 feet thick and 37 feet high. But the dam's designer had disastrously underestimated the power of the water that would one day surge against his immense structure. When, after heavy rains, a rushing torrent filled the wadi, the dam washed out.

More spectacular than this failure was a success scored by Egypt's engineers early in the second millennium B.C. With dikes and canals, they so regulated the inflow of water from the Nile to Lake Moeris in the desert west of Memphis that the lake became a great reservoir. It stored a portion of the river's overflow for use in irrigating the lush and fertile district known as the Faiyum.

The twin rivers of Mesopotamia

Even before Egyptian civilization arose out of the jungle-swamps of the Nile delta, Mesopotamian civilization had emerged from the delta marshes of the Tigris and Euphrates in what is today Iraq. But the water problems confronting the Mesopotamians were more difficult to solve than those of the Egyptians, for the floods of the Tigris and Euphrates, unlike the regular Nile floods, were unpredictable and variable.

Mesopotamians were concerned not only with flood control and irrigation but also with urban water supply and the creation of water highways for boats and barges. They developed a system of canals, dikes, reservoirs and simple dams that was probably much more complex than the Egyptians'. As early as 3000 B.C., every major Mesopotamian city was the centre of a canal network reaching to the outermost limits of the city's authority, and sometimes beyond.

Along the upper reaches of the twin rivers, home of the warlike Assyrians who dominated much of the Near East in the first millennium B.C., Mesopotamian engineers encountered a new difficulty—that of bringing water from distant mountains to supplement the supplies of their large cities. One of their canals, some 30 miles long, was built around 700 B.C. by the Assyrian King Sennacherib to supply fresh water to his capital of Nineveh. Part of its channel crossed a wide gully on one of the earliest great aqueducts of antiquity: it has been estimated that two million stone blocks went into its construction.

The most famous man-made waterway in ancient Mesopotamia was the 400-foot-wide Nahrwan Canal, used chiefly for irrigation. It paralleled the Tigris for more than 200 miles, from a point between the towns of Tikrit and Samarra to a little above Kut. Even by modern standards it was an impressive feat of hydraulic engineering, involving precise control of gradients over great distances and also the flow of river water into the dug channel, which may have been accomplished by means of sluice gates.

Life along the Indus

Fifteen hundred miles eastwards, a third great river civilization developed about 2500 B.C. It was geographically larger and, in some respects, more advanced technologically than those of either Egypt or Mesopotamia. Called the Harappan civilization after one of its cities unearthed by archaeologists, it flourished in the 1,000-mile-long, flood-washed valley of the river Indus that stretches from the Himalayas to the Arabian Sea. The 50 or so known sites, found mostly along the Indus and its tributaries, indicate that the Harappans depended upon the river primarily for irrigation but also for communication and trade.

All traces of the ancient Indus Valley irrigation systems have vanished, but such systems were probably as extensive and sophisticated as those of Mesopotamia. In addition, around Harappan cities—especially at the site of Mohenjo-Daro, 200 miles north of Karachi in West Pakistan—building foundations, dikes and drains have been excavated. From the frequency with which they seem to have been rebuilt, it is obvious that the Indus flooded them repeatedly.

Mohenjo-Daro was a mighty capital indeed, and some of its hydraulic achievements rival those of European cities today. For example, many private houses were two storeys high and had bathrooms, and the house drains were connected with covered sewers that run along the streets to join trunk lines emptying into cesspools.

The history of the fourth great river-nurtured civilization—that of the Hwang Ho of northern China—is comparatively obscure. The people who began to settle the lower plains of the river valley around 5000 B.C. met difficulties even greater than those faced by pioneers in the deltas of the Indus, Tigris-Euphrates and Nile. Besides having to drain and clear large marshes and forest-swamps, they had to cope with a far more unruly river and a severe climate.

THE GARDENS OF NINEVEH, in the seventh century B.C. Assyrian capital, had to get their water from mountain streams many miles away, even though the river Tigris ran right past the city. The river's flow was too uneven, so the ruler, Sennacherib, ordered the construction of an extensive system of canals and aqueducts to carry water from the mountains. A wall sculpture from an imperial palace (*below*) depicts a portion of the gardens, planted with fruit trees, herbs, vines and flowers —all flourishing on the transported water.

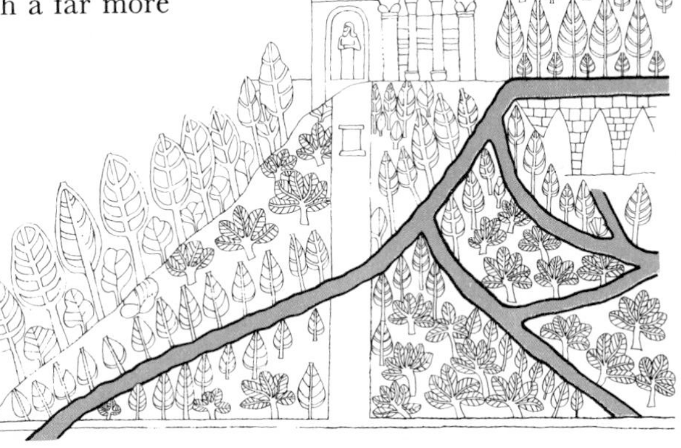

The Hwang Ho's mood changes from placid calm to violent rage, and for months each year the river is unnavigable, either frozen solid or clogged with floating ice in its lower reaches. Yet the Chinese laced its inhospitable valley with canals for communication and agriculture.

The Greeks, whose civilization flourished long after those of Egypt and Asia, left few conspicuous monuments of their hydraulic genius. The Romans, on the other hand, scattered throughout their vast empire grandiose works for supplying water to their cities. "If we take into careful consideration the abundant supplies of water in [Rome's] public buildings, baths, pools, open channels, private houses, gardens and country estates near the city," wrote Pliny the Elder, the great Roman naturalist of the first century A.D., "if we consider the distances traversed by the water before it arrives, the raising of arches, the tunnelling of mountains and the building of level routes across deep valleys, we shall readily admit that there has never been anything more remarkable in the whole world." Remarkable indeed these waterworks were—over truly imperial aqueducts they brought into Rome some 200 million gallons of water daily. This water was then distributed throughout the city by a complex system of lead pipes and stone and brick conduits.

Three of ancient Rome's 11 aqueducts continue in use today as part of that city's water system. The impressive remains of others stand in every Mediterranean land as testimony to Rome's hydraulic mastery. One, for example, built in Spain during the second century A.D., is almost perfectly preserved. On tiers of arches rising to a dizzying 90 feet or more above the street, it strides like some many-legged monster across the city of Segovia.

The four great civilizations created by rivers depended upon water not only to irrigate crops, but also for trade and communication—with their own towns and cities via rivers and canal and, by way of the sea, with foreign lands. Water served to nurture and unify civilization, and to spread it as well.

CHINA'S GRAND CANAL served for nearly 2,000 years as that country's principal north-south trade route, and also as a holiday route for emperors, who lined the waterway with ornate palaces and plantings. Begun in the sixth century B.C., the Grand Canal—like China's Great Wall—took centuries to complete and millions of people were employed in building it. The Canal's primary function was to link northern political centres with the rich farmlands of the south, but it was also used to control floods and to irrigate the land.

The master canal-builders

One of the most far-flung and intricate canal systems of antiquity was developed by the Chinese. Nearly all of China's rivers flow from west to east, and most of them were joined by a network of north-south waterways. The Grand Canal, running southwards from Peking to Hangchow on the river Tsientang, is about a thousand miles long—the longest waterway built by the ancients. It was begun in the sixth century B.C. and has been restored to partial use today.

In Egypt canals supplemented the Nile as arteries of travel and trade. A celebrated canal connected the Nile with the upper end of the Red Sea, speeding communication between Egypt and countries of western Asia. Probably first thrust through the desert about 600 B.C., it was repaired and rebuilt several times, once in 512 B.C. by a conqueror of Egypt—Persia's Darius the Great—after which it continued to be used for the next 1,300 years. When it was in full use, this huge ditch was said to be wide enough to accommodate two galleys rowed side by side.

As early as the third millennium B.C., Egyptian ships were sailing to the Syrian and East African coasts, and Mesopotamians were coasting Asia to the mouth of the Indus and possibly beyond. In succeeding centuries, merchant vessels launched by Cretans, Phoenicians, Greeks, Romans and others plied the ocean routes. Down through medieval times, goods from the East reached Europe largely by sea; within Europe commerce was supported by rivers and canals. But with the coming of the Industrial Revolution in the 18th and 19th centuries, water-borne traffic —particularly on canals—suddenly multiplied. Factories, mills and foundries demanded ever-increasing amounts of fuels and raw materials, much of which could be supplied only via waterways.

Waterways of industry

In England, focal point of the rising industrial civilization, a great boom in canal-building began about 1760, when James Brindley, who became the leading hydraulic engineer of his day, built one seven miles long to deliver coal from mines at Worsley to the textile-manufacturing town of Manchester. Later, in the 1790's, a "canal mania" swept England, Scotland and Ireland, and by 1830 canals in the British Isles totalled more than 3,000 miles. Canals were being increasingly built to service America's mushrooming industries by the beginning of the 19th century. The most famous of them, the Erie—built between 1817 and 1825 and now part of the New York State Barge Canal, giving access to industries of the Great Lakes—stretched over 350 miles of New York State, from Albany on the river Hudson to Buffalo on Lake Erie.

Although the rise of the railways led to a decline in the use of waterways, recently that trend has reversed. Shipping by water has always been cheaper than by rail. And the great post-war expansion of industry in Europe and America has led to a rebirth of inland waterways as principal routes of commerce.

In Europe many industrial centres are repairing their old canals and building new ones. One will be a new link between the river Rhone and the Rhine, bisecting the continent to allow water traffic between the North Sea and the Mediterranean. Other canals will eventually join most of the major cities in Germany, France, Belgium, the Netherlands and Luxembourg.

Probably no nation has made such a commercial virtue of a geographical necessity as the Netherlands. The intricate system of drainage and flood control that keeps the country from being submerged by the hostile sea also has provided it with the longest internal waterway system of any country in Europe. Nearly 5,000 of its more than 6,000 kilometres of commercially navigable waterways are canals. On these canals 174,000 tons of goods are transported annually, more tonnage than is carried by any other means.

The United States has a network of 25,600 miles of navigable rivers, canals and intracoastal waterways, and is still expanding this system. In 1963, for example, river barges for the first time in history hauled

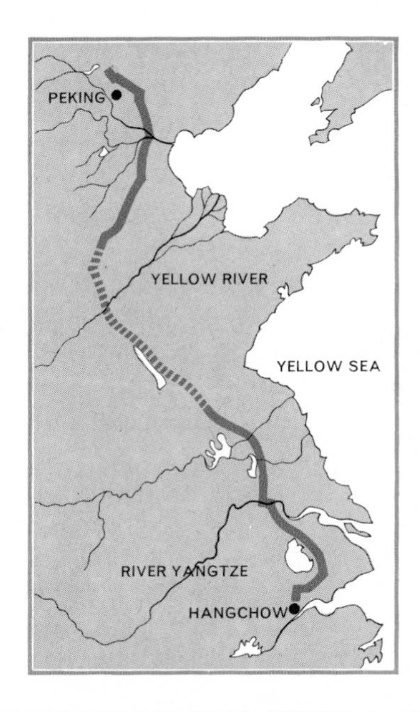

FROM HANGCHOW TO PEKING, the Grand Canal once stretched 1,000 miles across the eastern alluvial plains of China, often utilizing rivers along its course. It was about 100 feet wide at the narrowest point and at its peak carried more than two million tons of grain per year, in large wooden vessels. Since the turn of the century, many sections have fallen into disrepair and are now impassable (*dotted line*). Recently some of the old Canal has been restored—channels dredged and new locks installed—and some 680 miles are now reported navigable during part of the year.

more Midwestern grain to ports than U.S. railways. Its sheltered Atlantic Intracoastal Waterway stretches 1,300 miles, the length of the Eastern Seaboard, from New York to Florida. The St. Lawrence Seaway, jointly constructed and used by the United States and Canada, permits ocean-going vessels to sail directly to Great Lakes ports from the Atlantic Ocean—a distance of more than 2,000 miles inland.

The water that fosters civilization can also disrupt it. Too much or too little in an inconvenient place or at an inconvenient time can destroy cities, ruin crops or annihilate populations. Floods, droughts, tidal waves, blizzards and torrential rains, switching river-beds, rising or falling water-tables have ever harassed mankind.

The menace of the river

Of all nature's rampages, floods are especially destructive because people most often happen to be in the way. Almost all rivers have flooded at one time or another, but few have wrought so much havoc as the Hwang Ho. At least as early as the eighth century B.C. the Chinese were raising dikes to confine the shifting lower river in its channel. When the dikes gave way, as they have hundreds of times in the past 3,000 years, the damage was appalling.

The greatest flood devastation is caused by large rivers, not merely because they inundate larger areas. The larger the river, the longer it takes for the peak of the flood to pass and the longer the land stays under water. One of the large tributaries of the Ganga, the Kosi, flooded an area of more than 9,000 square miles during some of the worst floods in India's history in October and November, 1955. But the 1966 flood in Florence, Italy, which destroyed or damaged a million rare books and hundreds of art treasures, lasted only a day because of the smaller size of the Arno.

The great flood that inundates a plain rises gradually. Far more dramatic, and much more violent, is the sudden flood that surges through a mountain valley or a desert gully. Its coming is usually heralded by a short but heavy burst of rain. This is swiftly followed by the menacing sound of the flood rushing down the mountain-side. Behind a faint dust cloud, a brown horizontal line takes shape upstream and approaches like a great rug unrolling. It advances as fast as a man can run, ploughing before it a foam-flecked wave laden with sticks, brush, trees and fence posts. A second, smaller roaring wave may follow, and sometimes a third. The whole episode may be over in half an hour.

Such a flash flood occurred one night in 1959 above the small French Riviera town of Fréjus. A wall of water 25 feet high swept down the valley at a speed of 50 miles an hour, after bursting through the Malpasset dam, widely publicized as the world's thinnest major dam. A few hours later only ruins and mud coated the valley and 400 persons were dead.

Floods are natural to all rivers. A river's channel, though carved by the river itself, cannot cope with all the increased flow caused by exceptionally heavy storms and by great spring thaws. Some water must spill over—usually on to the flood-plain bordering the river channel.

Since man persists in settling and farming this floodable land—it is usually excellent farmland—he is asking for trouble. The advantages he obtains he must pay for either as flood losses or as the cost of works to protect him from the river. These costs total about £400 million a year in the United States alone.

Complete control of floods, like complete control of the weather, is beyond man's ability, but their havoc can be curbed. The simplest, most economical and most effective way is to restrict occupation and use of the flood-plain; this method has never been given an adequate trial because effective zoning restriction must be applied prior to rather than after urbanization. Flood damage is not easy to visualize until after it has occurred. Another way, and the one most commonly used, is to decrease a river's flood peaks by holding excess water temporarily in storage reservoirs. A third method is to confine flood-waters to the river's channel by levees, dikes or flood-walls.

Rarely are all flood-control techniques applied to any one river basin. But in some areas a combination of them has worked successfully.

For example, the previously mentioned tributary of the Ganga, the Kosi, had done incalculable damage in the past two centuries, for it had gradually moved its channel westwards some 70 miles. In 1954, India and Nepal agreed to build a dam near the river's source in Nepal and put up confining levees to hold the river in a fixed place. The levees extend 140 miles along the river and are placed about nine miles apart in some areas. This great width was necessary because of the braided character of the channel—consisting of many intertwining channels separated by islands.

The threat of 300 m.p.h. waves

Although river floods are the most widespread water disasters that menace mankind, there are others equally deadly—notably hurricane floods (high tides reinforced by high winds) and waves caused by seismic jolts or shiftings of the ocean's floor. These last—also known by their Japanese name, tsunami—are probably the most destructive forces of all. On the 1st April 1946, tsunamis created by an undersea convulsion near the Aleutians raced southwards at speeds up to 300 miles an hour and smashed without warning into the Hawaiian Islands. One towering wave after another tore away houses, ripped up concrete piers, hurled boats into the tree-tops. Damage totalled nearly £10 million; 173 people lost their lives.

Since then, seismographic warning stations have been set up at strategic points around the Pacific. Their delicate instruments quickly pinpoint an earthshock of tsunami potential so that endangered areas can be evacuated before the waves strike.

Over the ages, water has enabled man to irrigate his crops, raise great civilizations, spread his cultures and commerce over the face of the earth. But water also remains one of nature's greatest levellers of man and his works. Advancing science and technology sometimes help to minimize the hazards of rampaging water—yet, even today, man remains essentially at the mercy of this capricious element.

Profile of a Great River

The river Ganga (known as the Ganges before India's independence) presents a profile common to all great rivers as it pours down from its fountain-head in the Himalayas, meanders across hundreds of miles of flat plains, and dumps vast amounts of silt into a delta. It expends its energy in ways that affect millions of people. In remote mountains too rugged for roads, it cuts gorges that make travel possible (for example, they are the only route between India and Nepal). Near cities it serves both as a sewer and a source of drinking water. On plains, its flood-waters spread fertile soil without which crops could not flourish.

But a river's influence on a nation goes beyond the effects of water or silt. Distinctive cultures have taken shape along such rivers as the Mississippi, the Nile and the Ganga. Hindus consider the Ganga's water holy: multitudes of pilgrims bathe in it to wash away their sins; others climb the breathless heights of the Himalayas to visit the sacred headwaters. In commerce, in agriculture, in religion, the Ganga, like every great river, exerts a profound influence on the land and on the people who dwell along its banks.

A RIVER'S GROWTH
The icy waters of the Ganga rush down a deep Himalayan gorge about 25 miles downstream from the river's source in Gangotri Glacier. Along its first 160 miles, the Ganga is joined by several large tributaries and hundreds of smaller streams flowing through similar mountain gorges. The waters which feed the Ganga are gathered over a total watershed area of 376,000 square miles.

THE GANGA'S FOUNTAIN-HEAD
At the cave called the Cow's Mouth, 12,960 feet above sea level, pilgrims bathe in the Ganga. The river emerges from the bottom of the ice wall on the left. Among the hazards pilgrims face here are the boulders lodged on top of the glacier, which often tumble down without warning.

A TEMPLE ON THE TORRENT
Gangotri, a temple 15 miles below the Cow's Mouth, is surrounded by boulders disgorged by the glacier and washed down by the river (*below*). About 20,000 pilgrims get this far every year, but the trek on to the Cow's Mouth is so gruelling that only about 200 try it annually.

The Genesis of the Ganga

Most rivers are fed by rain, springs or lakes; some, like the Ganga, originate in glaciers. High in the Himalayas near the Tibetan frontier is Gangotri Glacier. Far up on the glacier's face, snow melts in the summer sun and seeps down into deep fissures in the ice. Rivulets merge into a torrent that burrows beneath the glacier through an eerie labyrinth of hidden cracks and crevices. The Ganga finally bursts into the open as a gushing river through the wall of an ice cave called Gaumukh, a Hindu word that means "the Cow's Mouth".

Gangotri Glacier stretches through 16 miles of valley, winding between high Himalayan peaks. At the Cow's Mouth, 12,960 feet above sea level, the glacier is about half a mile wide. Over the last million years the glacier has receded about 29 miles—it once terminated at a point only 8,200 feet above sea level. Survey parties have tried to ascend the glacier countless times. Almost all have been driven back, however, by avalanches, storms, and impassable crevices in the ice.

A ROAD ON A ROCKY WALL

A huge chunk of cliff disappears in a cloud of smoke and debris as engineers blast a new road through a Himalayan pass. If it were not for such gorges, cut by rivers, the mountains would be totally impassable. The few roads that exist are narrow, rocky ledges built along the rock slopes. Even these are closed down by snow and avalanches during most of the year.

A DOMESTICATED RIVER

Indians wash their clothes at the edge of the Ganga near Benares. The Ganga supplies year-round water for all the domestic needs of people living along its banks. Its flow, however, varies greatly with the seasons. In the driest season, water flows at the rate of 60,000 cubic feet per second. In times of flood, the flow may swell to 25 million cubic feet per second.

A Watery Clash of Colours

As it flows across the plains, the Ganga is so full of silt that its waters are a muddy yellow or brown. In striking contrast is the clear-blue river Jamuna, which originates in the Himalayas only 40 miles from the Ganga. Throughout its 860-mile course, it never strays more than 75 miles from the Ganga. But when the two rivers come together at Allahabad, they meet with a dramatic clash of colours.

The difference results from the

Hindus row out to drop funeral ashes at the spot where the Ganga meets the Jamuna. Where ashes are cast on the water, petals are also

sort of bed each river has built for itself. Although both streams drop from the Himalayas, and each is tapped near its base to irrigate the plains (together they irrigate more than a million acres), the similarities end there. The Ganga flows over a bed of silt it has deposited during past centuries. The Jamuna flows in a rocky bed on a higher plateau near the foot of the Vindhya Mountains, and it is replenished along the way by clear streams that rush from mountain gorges. Veering across the plain, it finally empties into the silt-laden Ganga—but even 50 miles downstream patches of blue can be seen amid the muddy swells of the Ganga.

strewn. On holy days, as many as four million pilgrims have tried to bathe here at once; on one occasion 500 Hindus died in the crush.

A River Serving as a Sewer

At Benares the Ganga becomes an urban sewer. Waste from the city's 650,000 people flushes into the river through ancient stone drains. Ashes from funeral pyres also are cast in, as are the corpses of sacred cows. The Indians drink and bathe in this water; as a result many have acquired some immunity to infection, but many others doubtless fall ill from the polluted water. A modern filtration and pumping station exists, but few drink the piped water, feeling that filtration destroys its holiness. According to the faithful, "It lies not in man's power to pollute the Ganga".

PRAYER AND POLLUTION
A pilgrim recites her prayers in the Ganga amid dancing reflections of Benares at sunrise. Before departing from the holy city, pilgrims bottle some of the polluted river water for use at home.

A STAIRWAY TO THE GANGA
Pilgrims bathe near one of the ghats—steps that lead into the water—that line the Ganga at Benares. Many elderly people, having come here to die, are cremated on similar steps. All of India's 370 million Hindus try to wash in the river's water at least once during their lives.

Seasons of Flood and Drought

The Ganga is a river of extremes. In the season of the incessant and torrential monsoon rains (one town had a 46-inch deluge in a single day), the river overflows its banks near the mouth and the countryside lies inundated for months. In the season of the drought, temperatures rise above 42°C., and the river retreats within its banks; over the months the land becomes a virtual desert.

The severity of the water cycle along the Ganga is a source of both the land's prosperity and its troubles. The deep silt deposited by the river over the centuries is fertile and easily worked. Farmers on the floodplain raise rice, which must be planted under water; some harvest two crops in the three-month wet season. For the other nine months, raising crops requires extensive irrigation.

Farming in this fashion has been called "a gamble in rain". The Gangetic plain, which is about the same size as Peru, has close to 20 times the Peruvian population. If the rains are late, the result is often famine: in 1957, during an extended drought, 25 million Indians were stricken.

WATER FOR A DRY LAND
A water-wheel, used to irrigate crops planted shortly before the monsoon, is powered by a camel yoked to a cross-beam and treading in a circle. The beam runs a set of gears that are connected to the wheel. Water is drawn from a stone well in which rain from the past monsoon is stored. During droughts, such wells and the Ganga itself are the only source of water.

CROPS IN A SOAKED LAND
Surrounded by green fields of rice and sugar cane, a village lies drenched by monsoon rains. On the central plains the Ganga (*top left*) swells during the monsoon but rarely floods. Near the delta, however, floods are so common that the towns are built on high earth foundations.

A River Rarely Spanned

The Ganga is northern India's main artery of trade and travel. Boats of every description ply its waters: flatboats and barges, steamers and scows, sailing-boats and skiffs. Thousands of boatmen spend their lives at the oars of cargo craft, drawing an average wage of less than 2 shillings a day.

Although railways and highways run beside the Ganga, in many places a boat is the only way to cross the river. The Gangetic plain is covered with a blanket of silt (a quarter of a mile thick in some spots). This makes it extraordinarily difficult to find support for heavy bridge pilings. Only about 12 bridges span the whole river, although temporary pontoon bridges are often used. When the 1.1-mile span of the Ganga bridge near Patna was erected in 1959, its massive foundations had to be sunk nearly 200 feet deep, requiring about 32,000 tons of concrete. The chance of spanning the Ganga has seemed so small that two railways built along its opposite banks use tracks of different gauge.

TRADING BY BARGE
Straining against the current, sweating oarsmen row a barge along the Ganga. They often travel hundreds of miles upstream, hawking their merchandise to villagers along the way. They live on the barge, and sometimes stay out on the river as long as nine months at a time

COMMUTING BY FERRY
A side-wheeler carries Indian commuters across the Ganga near Patna. All boats on the river, including large steamers like this one, must be flat-bottomed or shallow-draught vessels because the Ganga, although two miles wide at some points, is often no more than a few feet deep.

A straw-laden barge is floated to mills near Patna. The city's moorings often have 20 to 30 such boats lined up waiting to be loaded.

The Muddy Demise of a Mighty Stream

About 1,300 miles from its fountainhead in the Himalayas, the Ganga finally strangles on its own silt. Its main channel, too shallow for large ships, flows into East Pakistan. The rest of the Ganga's muddy waters regroup into other rivers that wearily inch southwards across an immense delta, deserting old channels which have been choked with silt, cutting new ones, and finally seeping into the Bay of Bengal through dozens of mouths.

On one of these rivers, the Hooghly, stands the bustling port of Calcutta, 128 miles in from the sea. Keeping the Hooghly navigable from port to sea is an endless operation that keeps 18 dredges at work around the clock. In 1963 this fleet dredged 8,206,023 tons of silt from the river, working a total of 5,781 hours at a cost of £820,000. The silt is ultimately dumped at the mouth of the river. The fleet includes the biggest dredger in the world, a £1.5-million ship that can suck up 100,000 cubic feet of silt (about 4,500 tons) every 50 minutes. This dredger alone has a crew of 18 officers and 92 deck-hands.

A PORT IN SACRED WATERS
Hindus take a ritual bath beside a dilapidated Calcutta pier as commercial vessels loom in the distance. Calcutta is one of the busiest ports in Asia. In one year (spanning 1963-1964) a total of 1,828 cargo vessels entered the port. These ships carried 5,932,825 tons of incoming cargo. During the same period 4,832,745 tons of exports were shipped out of Calcutta

7

The All-Purpose Substance

TUNNEL LINERS WAIT ASSEMBLY ON THE SITE OF A HUGE MULTIPURPOSE DAM AT FORK PECK, MONTANA. THEY DIVERTED THE RIVER MISSOURI WHILE THE DAM WAS BEING BUILT.

A Motor-Car coming off the assembly line represents the expenditure of at least 25,000 gallons of water—17,000 needed to produce its ton of steel, and 8,000 more used during the actual assembly process. Many thousands more are involved in the manufacture of its plastics, glass, fabrics and other parts. Every gallon of petrol poured into the tank may represent as much as another 60 gallons of water, utilized in refining.

Statistics like these could be prepared for every amenity of civilized society—for the food we eat, the clothes we wear, even the books we read and the television we watch. For water is the life-blood of industry, its most essential material. No other substance except air flows in such volume through the factories of the industrialized world. Water is a source of power, either directly in hydroelectric plants, or indirectly as steam. It supplies the warmth that radiates from many heating systems, and in steel mills its coolness quenches glowing metal. It is a raw material in chemicals, beer, pharmaceuticals and hundreds of other products. It is the solvent in which chemical reactions take place in the manufacture of bleaches, and it washes impurities from pulp in paper mills. Via streams and rivers, it carries off many thousands of tons of industrial waste daily.

All these uses—plus many more—are possible because of water's chemical and physical properties, such as its heat capacity and solvent power.

Since early in history, men have put these properties to work. And to make them work more efficiently, they have created ever more ingenious devices, for water has long been a mother of inventions.

The earliest way of employing water was to pour it upon a field for irrigation. This could be hard work, but in Mesopotamia by the third millennium B.C., and later in Egypt, farmers found a way to make the job easier—by combining human sinew with a simple lever machine called the shaduf, still widely used in the Orient and the Middle East. The shaduf was a beam resting in a notch on top of a broad post. A leather bucket hung from one end of the beam, and a counterweight was attached to the other. After the farmer had dipped the bucket into a stream, the counterweight helped him to lift the bucket high enough to dump the water into a ditch running among his crops. Crude as it was, the shaduf enabled a man to raise 500 gallons of water a day to a height of six feet much more easily than he could by muscle power alone.

Centuries later, some genius hit upon the idea of lifting water by means of pots fastened about the rim of a vertical wheel. As the wheel revolved, turned by one or more men walking a treadmill attached to its shaft, one pot after another scooped up water, raised it, and spilt it into the irrigation ditch. An adaptation of this device—an endless chain carrying buckets—may have been used to water the Hanging Gardens of Babylon in the sixth century B.C.

Later still, Archimedes of Syracuse (287-212 B.C.), one of the great scientific intellects of all time, is believed to have invented the water screw which bears his name. In principle similar to the modern kitchen meat grinder, Archimedes' screw consisted of thin wooden strips coiled on edge in a spiral around a rod and tightly encased in a wooden tube. One end of the tube was immersed in the stream, the other inclined upwards to rest on the lip of an irrigation trench. The farmer spun the whole thing with a hand crank. As the tube revolved, water was trapped in each turn of the screw and raised until it came out at the top. The Romans called Archimedes' invention a cochlea (snail), and used it to drain their tin mines in Britain. In some Mediterranean countries, farmers still spin a modification of the water screw.

Water to mark the hours

These were prosaic devices to transport water where men wanted it. Other inventions were more exotic. There was, for instance, the water clock, or clepsydra, probably first used in ancient Egypt. This was a jar with one or several holes in its bottom. The time it took for a given amount of water to drip completely out of the jar became a measuring unit. In the courts of early Greece, speeches were limited by such a clock—time ran out when the water ran out. With this primitive system, it was easy enough to measure a cupful of time, but determining intermediate intervals was difficult since the water did not flow at a constant rate. When the cup was full, it leaked out faster because the water pressure was high. As the water level decreased, so did the pressure, and the leak slowed to a leisurely drip.

The problem of reckoning intermediate time intervals was solved around 250 B.C. by Ctesibius, a Greek barber-turned-engineer. Ctesibius built a clepsydra that transformed a slender stream of water into a stream of time. His timekeeper consisted of three vessels. The first was the source of water. Through a hole in its bottom, water dripped into a second vessel in which the water level was kept constant by an overflow outlet part way up the vessel's side. Another outlet in the bottom of the vessel released water at a uniform rate into the third vessel. The sides of this third vessel could be marked off in graduated units on which the rising water level indicated the time.

Eventually clepsydras became elaborate affairs involving gears, wheels and shafts. The Roman architect-engineer Vitruvius, in his celebrated work *De architectura*, written about 25 B.C., told of one such clock in which "figures are moved, cones revolve, pebbles or eggs fall, trumpets sound, and other incidental effects take place".

In the first century A.D. the first clue to the use of water for steam power was uncovered by another Greek mechanical genius, Hero of Alexandria. Hero, whose inventions ranged from a bellows-operated organ to a coin-in-the-slot holy-water dispenser, produced the aeolipile—a hollow sphere partially filled with water and suspended between two pivot supports over a fire. When the water boiled, tubes on either side of the sphere, their openings bent to face in opposite directions, emitted jets of steam. The reaction to the jets, like the reaction to the blast from a modern rocket engine, caused the sphere to whirl furiously. Al-

ARCHIMEDES' PUMP was presumably invented by the Greek geometer in the third century B.C., and was used for irrigation. The pump consisted of a hollow wooden tube within which there was a spiral screw thread wound around a central pole (*section above*). Cranked by hand, it raised water from a river to a field above it. The Nile delta has been irrigated with such devices for centuries.

though Hero's toy was the first steam-engine, its inventor put it to no practical use.

The truly epoch-making hydraulic inventions of antiquity, however, were those that first harnessed the energy inherent in falling water.

The simplest water-wheel, probably invented for milling grain in the Near or Middle East about the first century B.C., had a series of paddles fanning out from a vertical shaft, like a wheel laid on its side. The shaft passed upwards through a hole in a fixed, horizontal millstone and was fastened to a movable millstone on top. Such a mill was usually built at the edge of a swift stream so that some of its paddles extended into the current. The current, pushing against the paddles, turned the shaft and the upper millstone. Grain placed between the stones was ground to flour, but the grinding was a slow process—one revolution of the water-wheel meant one revolution of the millstone. But slow as they were, such primitive mills served man for two millennia. One was still operating in the Shetland Islands off northern Scotland as late as the 1930's. This type of mill, widely used in the fast-running streams of Northern Europe, became known as the Norse mill.

Wheels that crush grain

Far more efficient was the water-wheel named after Vitruvius, the same Roman author who described the water clock. The Vitruvian wheel was the water-wheel of the Norse mill turned on edge and mounted on a horizontal axle. It was what engineers call an undershot wheel—it revolved as water flowing under it struck the low paddles. A large gear on the wheel's horizontal axle engaged a smaller gear on the vertical millstone shaft. The rotary motion of the axle was thereby transmitted to the millstone so that it turned several times with each revolution of the water-wheel. Thus the Vitruvian mill was capable of producing more flour—and producing it faster—than the Norse mill.

All water-wheels are turned by the energy of descending water, and the theoretical maximum energy available for the job depends only on the height through which the water descends. When this drop occurs gradually, as it must in a stream supplying a Norse or undershot wheel, much of the theoretically available energy has been dissipated in friction before the water reaches the wheel. If the water can make all or most of its descent right at the wheel itself, more energy will be available for use. In addition, the descending water will be in contact with the paddles for a greater distance than in the case of an undershot wheel; thus more of the available energy will be applied to the motion of the wheel. By late Roman times these facts were recognized by some unknown engineer, and he introduced the overshot wheel—one turned by water that poured down on the upper paddles through a sluice leading from a dam at a higher level.

As long as manpower—especially slave labour—was plentiful, there was little incentive to develop water power extensively. But when Europe began to emerge from the Dark Ages that followed the collapse of the

Roman Empire and entered a period of economic growth, water power became increasingly important to its expanding industries. The Domesday Book, written in 1085 by order of William the Conqueror to record, among other things, the economic resources of England, lists 5,624 water mills—one for about every 400 inhabitants.

Soon water-wheels were being used for a wide variety of industrial purposes besides grinding grain. They powered machines to saw wood, spin silk, chop rags for paper-making, beat hides for tanning. They pumped the bellows for early blast furnaces. They ran trip-hammers to crush ore and shape metal. They turned polishing machines for armourers and, later, boring machines for gunsmiths. A 19th-century giant, $72\frac{1}{2}$ feet in diameter, developed 200 horsepower to drive a mine-draining pump on the Isle of Man in the Irish Sea.

The steam revolution

"By the middle of the 18th century," the American historian and critic Lewis Mumford has pointed out, "the fundamental industrial revolution . . . had been accomplished: the external forces of nature were harnessed and the mills and looms and spindles were working busily through Western Europe." The chief force of nature thus employed was water. But it was now beginning to be used in a completely different way: as steam. It was the harnessing of water, not simply as a falling weight, but as a substance with amazingly useful heat properties that brought on the Industrial Revolution as we think of it today.

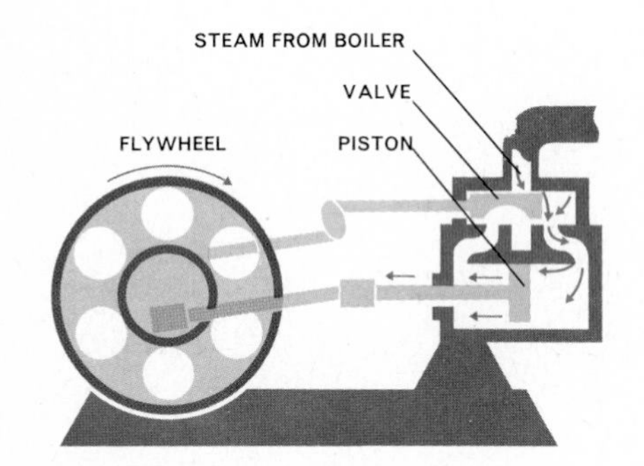

STEAM POWER, introduced in the 18th century, utilized water's tendency to expand when heated. In the reciprocating steam-engine above, the flywheel is operated by the thrusts of a piston that is driven to and fro by steam entering the cylinder from a boiler. A valve is moved to and fro by the flywheel; its purpose is to direct the steam alternately to the two sides of the piston.

The steam-engine works as well as it does precisely because of the peculiar physical properties of water. For one thing, water becomes steam at a moderate temperature, a temperature low enough to have been within the capabilities of 17th- and 18th-century machine builders. But most important is water's ability to absorb heat. A very large quantity of heat energy is needed to raise the temperature of water a given number of degrees or to change it from a liquid to a gas. Conversely, the change from gas to liquid releases a great amount of heat energy. This energy is the source of the work done by a steam-engine; it is converted into mechanical energy to drive pumps, turn wheels and operate looms.

The heat energy that water (or any substance) absorbs increases the motion of its molecules. The more heat, the faster the molecules jump around. At a certain speed—i.e., at a certain temperature—they jump so fast that they overcome the forces that link them together: the liquid boils and becomes a gas. Breaking such a link requires a great amount of energy; at this point the energy is absorbed simply to cause the transformation without increasing temperature. This change from liquid into gas is accompanied by a sudden increase in volume. When water boils into steam, it expands some 1,600 times. Further heating increases the molecular motion still more, causing even greater expansion.

The first crude engine to utilize the expansion created when water changes to steam was invented in 1690 by Denis Papin, a French Huguenot physicist living in England. Papin put a small amount of water into a tube about two and a half inches in diameter that was closed at the bottom and fitted with a snug piston. When he brought the water to a boil, the expanding steam forced the piston to the top of the tube, where a catch secured it. Then Papin cooled the tube, and the steam condensed into the original volume of water, leaving a partial vacuum in the tube. When the catch was released, the outside air pressure drove the piston back with a snap.

A few years later, a military engineer named Thomas Savery, sitting in a tavern on the Cornish coast, was startled to see a cork being sucked *into* a bottle half full of steaming hot water. A few experiments showed him that when bottles of steaming water were set in a cool place, the corks were always pulled in as the steam condensed. Savery then built this principle into a crude steam pump that managed to drain water from several mine pits. The pump consisted of two parts which operated alternately. Each part was made up of a closed, barrel-shaped vessel equipped with valves and two pipes. When one vessel was filled with steam from a boiler, then suddenly cooled with a dash of cold water, the steam condensed, creating a partial vacuum in the vessel. Through a pipe leading from the vessel to the drainage pit of the mine, water was sucked up into the vessel. When the steam was turned on again, the water was forced upwards through an outlet pipe. Then the process was repeated. Because its lifting power was inadequate, Savery's pump was never widely used.

A mechanical seesaw

In 1705 Thomas Newcomen, a Devonshire ironmonger and smith, built the first practical steam engine, again for use in the mines. Newcomen combined Savery's separate boiler with Papin's moving piston and cylinder and added an idea of his own, a huge wooden cross-beam—a seesaw arrangement with one end connected to a counterweight and a pump rod extending down in the mine, the other end attached to the piston in the cylinder. When steam was forced into the cylinder, the piston was raised to the top. Then, from a separate water tank, cold water was piped into the cylinder to cool the steam. As the steam condensed into water a partial vacuum formed in the cylinder and atmospheric pressure drove the piston back, as the cork was drawn into Savery's bottle of cooling water. When more steam was forced into the cylinder, the piston moved up again and the cycle was repeated, rocking the beam up and down, to operate the pump and drain the mine. This engine did not make full use of the tremendous power of expanding steam—but it was the first machine with moving parts driven partly by steam, although it also utilized the pressure of the atmosphere.

The atmospheric pump was useful but expensive, requiring mountains of coal to keep it running. The man who solved this problem was James Watt, a young instrument maker for Glasgow University. While repairing a Newcomen engine one day in 1763, Watt began to wonder why it required so much fuel. It was obvious that less fuel would be needed if the cylinder did not have to be heated and cooled over and over again —that is, if it could be kept constantly as hot as the steam coming into it. If the steam could be transferred to a separate chamber before it was condensed, there would be no need to cool the cylinder at all. Watt first tested his idea on a small model, using a surgeon's 10-inch brass syringe as cylinder-and-piston. In a later, improved version of his engine, he insulated the cylinder in an outer casing that could be filled with steam, to keep the cylinder constantly hot. Then he rigged up a separate chamber kept cool by cold water. When the steam from his boiler filled the cylinder, it forced its way through a tube into the cooling chamber, where it condensed into water. Meanwhile, the expanding steam drove the piston in the cylinder.

Watt caused this transformation from steam into water to occur outside the cylinder, thereby making it possible for the cylinder to be kept hot and the condenser cool at the same time. But engineers who followed him concentrated on getting more and more energy from the expansion of steam by heating it to higher and higher temperatures; this way it could expand more, and perform more work.

Watt devised a way of introducing steam at both ends of the cylinder alternately, thereby getting two power strokes where before there had been only one. (Later came the double-expansion engine, and even triple- and quadruple-expansion engines, in which steam from a first cylinder was led to a second and allowed to continue expanding, putting still more of its energy to work.)

A nation "steam mill mad"

Finally, prodded by his business partner, Matthew Boulton, who wrote to him in 1781 that "the people of London, Manchester, and Birmingham are *steam mill mad*", Watt contrived a practical mechanical linkage that could convert the up-and-down motion of the reciprocating steam engine into rotary motion. At last the steam-engine was ready to fulfil its role as the prime mover of 19th-century industry and transportation.

Today the steam piston engine has been largely replaced by the steam turbine, invented in 1882 by a Swedish engineer, Carl Gustaf Patrik de Laval, who was looking for a device to spin a high-speed cream separator. Laval was a specialist in the design of nozzles, and he knew that the steam jet from one of his sand-blasting nozzles could spin the entire sand-blasting machine. This was the germ of his idea.

All turbines are bladed wheels. Like the steam piston engine, a steam turbine stores heat energy and releases it in a usable form as the steam expands and cools. In the modern turbine, expanding steam is squirted from nozzles to rotate a wheel rimmed with blades. The blades are so shaped that the steam leaves them in a high-velocity jet. The impact of the entering steam striking the turbine helps to turn the wheel, much as water striking the paddles turns a water-wheel, but it is the reaction to the departing steam—the kickback—which provides the major driving force. Then the steam passes through a ring of stationary blades which serve to squirt it in jets against another rotor. The process is repeated, with the steam expanding at each step until the last available energy has been wrested from it.

There are water turbines, too. Like the overshot water-wheel which first turned millstones in the closing years of the Roman Republic, these exploit the energy released by falling water. As the steam turbine derives its major driving force from reaction to exiting steam, so many water turbines get their chief power from the exiting stream of water.

Because turbines produce smooth rotary motion they are particularly suited to the generation of electricity. Some 30 years after the dynamo was invented in 1831, water was harnessed to the work of driving it with a reciprocating steam-engine. Today, steam or water turbines perform this job.

Power from harnessed water

Predictably, the first large hydroelectric power plant in the United States was built at Niagara Falls, in 1895. By 1968, more than 1,500 hydroelectric plants were helping to light homes and run factories. Of the more than one million million kilowatt-hours of electricity produced for general distribution in the United States each year, steam plants provide 79 per cent and hydroelectric plants about 20 per cent (about 1 per cent is produced by internal-combustion engines). Together they make use of some 350 million million gallons of water.

One of the most impressive works of modern engineering is a great dam producing hydroelectric power. Hoover Dam, towering 726 feet above the bed of the river Colorado between Nevada and Arizona and backed by its 115-mile-long reservoir of Lake Mead, is a spectacular example. The most famous dam in the Western Hemisphere—and the tallest—it attracts thousands of sightseers each year. Lifts from the top of the dam lower visitors 528 feet into the heart of the vast concrete structure—a distance equal to 44 storeys in an office building—to a tunnel connecting with the power plant at the dam's base. Each wing of the U-shaped plant is as long as two football fields laid end to end and houses a row of the plant's 17 giant generators. On a level below the roaring generators are the turbines, spun by water flowing under tremendous pressure through four main pipes, or penstocks, from Lake Mead. These penstocks are enormous, each 30 feet in diameter and large enough to carry a railway train or two lanes of highway traffic. When the water has done its work of spinning the turbines and their genera-

IN A STEAM TURBINE, superheated steam (*blue arrows*) blasts against vanes attached to the turbine's shaft, causing the shaft to spin. The resulting energy may be used for a variety of purposes, from powering a luxury liner to operating an electric power plant. The steam enters a turbine at pressures up to 400 pounds per square inch, but it loses some pressure within the engine. As it does so it expands—and the cylinder is made wide at the far end to allow for the expansion.

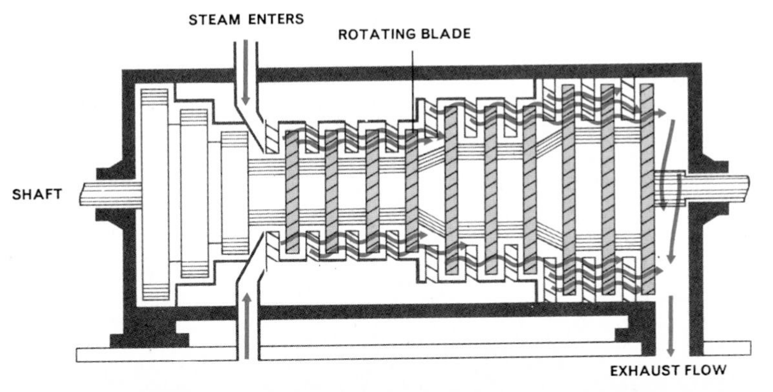

tors to produce electrical energy, it gushes from turbine discharge tubes at the base of the dam into the churning gorge of the river Colorado.

The huge dams used in producing electricity are usually designed to serve other needs as well—for example, they store water for irrigating farmland, and create lakes for fishing and boating. The best-known example of such multipurpose planning is the Tennessee Valley Authority, a government corporation created in 1933 to develop the full potential of the great Tennessee River system. In addition to generating hydroelectric power, it helps to control erosion, provides recreation facilities and improves navigation. Its vast system of dams, reservoirs, steam plants and bridges ranks it among the world's great engineering projects.

A river system revitalized

At the outset, TVA took over the already built Wilson Dam at Muscle Shoals, Alabama. It has since acquired 3 major dams, built 22 new ones and integrated 6 others into its system. Altogether, these have made the river Tennessee navigable for 650 miles from Knoxville, Tennessee, to its mouth at the Ohio. The dams supply electric power over an area of 80,000 square miles. New and improved fertilizers developed by TVA have helped thousands of valley farmers to enrich their soil, revitalizing a countryside that was once among the poorest regions in the United States. Since TVA was established, the population of the Tennessee Valley has increased by more than a million; its *per capita* income rose from 45 per cent of the national average in 1933 to over 70 per cent in 1968.

Electric power production was a vital part of the original TVA conception and remains by far the best-known feature of its economic activity. But the power, at first largely hydroelectric, is now about 80 per cent steam-produced. The increase in steam-generating capacity began in response to the needs of the government-owned atomic energy plants situated near by, and accelerated with the advance of industrialization and living standards in the area.

TVA's over-all benefits have inspired ideas for similar river developments elsewhere in the world. Outstanding among them is the Volta River Project in Ghana, which has provided one of the underdeveloped areas of the world with the power-producing potential necessary for a modern industrialized State. The idea of harnessing the Volta was first proposed in 1915 by A. E. Kitson, an Australian geologist who travelled the river by canoe. Bauxite had been discovered, and Kitson suggested that a dam near Akosombo, where the river passes through a gorge before descending to the lowlands, could provide the power to process the ore. When the dam was finally completed in 1966, the £160 million Volta River complex produced 512 million watts of electricity—20 times Gha-

HYDROELECTRIC PLANTS, generating electric power from dammed-up water, produce 20 per cent of the U.S. power supply. Building up behind a high dam, water accumulates potential energy. This is transformed into kilowatts when the water rushes down a sluice and is diverted into the rotary blades of a turbine (a refined version of the ancient water-wheel). The turbine's rotation spins electromagnets which generate current in stationary coils of wire. Finally, the current is put through an adjoining transformer where the voltage is stepped up for transmission over power lines.

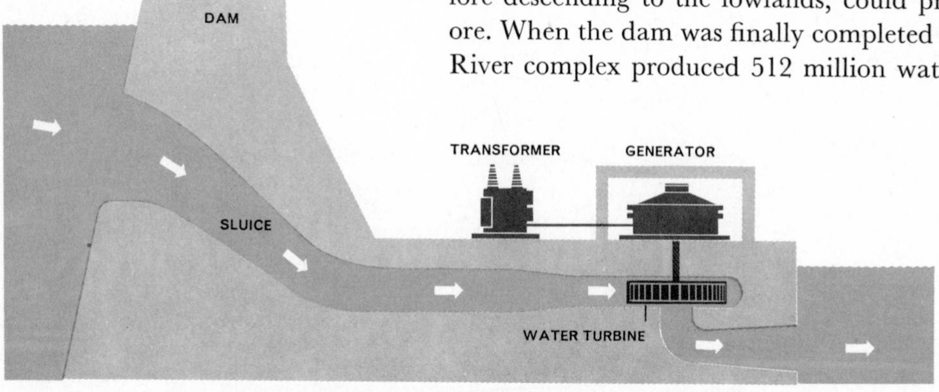

na's 1960 output. Its potential is 786 million watts, half of which is intended for the large aluminium smelter at the port city of Tema, while the other half will provide power for Ghana's expanding industry as well as for sale to its neighbouring countries. The dam also created a 3,275-square-mile artificial lake that added a thriving fishing industry, cheap water transport and irrigation for 6,000 square miles of cultivable land.

Although multipurpose projects such as TVA and the Volta River Project development appear to be ideal integrated river-basin plans which have bettered the lives of the people living in the region, they do have inherent shortcomings. To justify the construction of reservoirs, it is often pointed out that they can be made to serve many uses—but it is rarely recognized that these uses may be competitive. In order to provide flood protection, a reservoir should be kept as empty as possible so that there will be space to store flood-water when it comes. For irrigation or water-supply purposes, on the other hand, a reservoir should be at near-capacity level as insurance against dry periods. Also, power production is enhanced by a full reservoir because the generation of power increases or decreases in accordance with the depth of the water. Obviously, no one reservoir can serve all purposes simultaneously.

The value of scenery

Other shortcomings of multipurpose projects—and those least often appreciated—are imponderables involving values to society as a whole. Advanced societies, and the United States in particular, have needs and desires transcending mere money values. An example of this is the nation's present interest in its natural beauty. Dams and reservoirs can be evaluated in terms of monetary costs and monetary benefits, but comparable yardsticks to measure aesthetic value—the existence of unspoiled scenery, of wilderness solitude, of recreation—do not exist. Nevertheless, the value of a contemplated reservoir must be balanced against the worth of the same area preserved for its aesthetic quality. These aesthetic values are increasing and will continue to increase with scarcity, particularly in this age of population pressure. The reservoir of Glen Canyon Dam on the river Colorado in northern Arizona already encroaches on the magnificence of Rainbow Bridge National Monument, and dams for power generation are being contemplated that would alter the spectacularly beautiful and unique landscape of the Grand Canyon. One of these would create a man-made lake stretching for 93 miles through the world-famous river gorge.

Thus great water-development projects can prove both a liability and a blessing. Efficiently conceived, they can bring prosperity and well-being to vast areas of the world. Improperly planned, they can create problems that may more than outweigh their benefits.

Putting Water to Work

If man had been content to leave water where nature put it, his civilization might have stopped growing long ago. Instead he has stored water in reservoirs, converted its energy into electricity; channelled it into canals, moved it great distances to irrigate farms, employed it in industrial processes and pushed it back with dikes to gain more land.

The process of controlling the earth's water has driven man to undertake the largest of all his engineering projects. The two-mile-long Aswan High Dam on the Nile—110 million tons of granite rock, sand and concrete that backs up a lake more than 300 miles long—more than doubled Egypt's power production. Irrigation conduits in Israel carry water 70 miles to make a desert bloom. A navigation canal in China stretches 1,000 miles; the mighty locks of the Panama Canal lift cargo ships over an 85-foot-high ribbon of land that separates oceans. In France, a new type of dam has been designed to harness the flow of the tide. The scope of water-control engineering is constantly expanding to meet the needs of growing populations. Every month, another major dam is completed somewhere in the world.

DETOUR FOR A RIVER

Before concrete could be poured for the Bhakra Dam in India, two tunnels 50 feet in diameter had to be bored through solid rock around both sides of the dam site to divert the river's flow. Each of the tunnels carried water half a mile at the rate of five feet per second. When the dam was completed, the two tunnels were plugged with several hundred thousand tons of concrete.

Taming Mighty Rivers

Dams, the biggest of all man-made structures, are designed to serve a number of purposes: they back up reservoirs for irrigation, store municipal water, produce electric power, improve navigation and protect against floods. Most dams hold back water by their sheer weight. Known as gravity dams, they can be made of earth, rock or concrete. Another type of dam, used especially in narrow gorges, employs the structural strength of an arch, in addition to weight, to hold back rivers.

Dams are breeders of impressive statistics. The Kariba Dam (*right*) on the river Zambesi between Rhodesia and Zambia cost an estimated £113 million and required as many as 7,000 African labourers at one time. Before it could be built, workmen put up a series of cofferdams to divert water around the dam's site. More than a million cubic yards of concrete were used to build the great curved wall. The completed dam has a capacity of 130 million acre feet or nearly 35 million gallons of water.

A BULWARK FOR THE ZAMBESI
The Kariba Dam is a concrete structure 420 feet high—more than twice the height of Niagara Falls—and measures 2,025 feet across its crest. Completed in 1960, it generates electricity for both Rhodesia and Zambia and supplies water to irrigate 200,000 acres of land in the Zambesi Valley. Behind it now lies the 2,000-square mile Lake Kariba, largest man-made lake in the world.

A THIN TIE TO SURVIVAL
A stone aqueduct, built between the hills of Kweichow province in southern China, bears water to a patchwork of rice fields in an impoverished region consisting mostly of mountain ridges and narrow valleys. The 65,000-square-mile province has no major river. The terraced rice fields, many of them set into the hill-sides, are irrigated by the flooding method.

Watering a Wasteland

If rainfall in a warm climate averages less than 20 inches a year, the land cannot be farmed for most crops unless it is irrigated. Although such regions may lie hundreds of miles from a river, they can be made to bloom through the agency of modern engineering. A single dam on the river Yangtze in China is designed to disperse water to 10 million arid acres. Many irrigation projects, such as that of the United States' Central Valley in California (*left*), receive their water via broad concrete canals. Sometimes the water is transported by pipelines or along stone aqueducts (*far left*).

There is about three times as much irrigated land in the world today as there was at the turn of the century. The total is approaching 350 million acres, with the greatest concentrations in the vast land areas of China, India and Pakistan, the U.S. and Russia. However, irrigation also poses a serious problem. Nearly 97 per cent of the water for houses or factories is flushed back into rivers and can be treated and re-used. But in irrigation, almost all the water is lost—through evaporation, transpiration by plants, and seepage through canal beds which are not lined with concrete.

CARRYING WATER TO NEEDY SOIL
Curving through the Central Valley, an irrigation canal brings a heavy flow of water from the reservoir behind California's Shasta Dam in the U.S. Once a barren area of cactus and sagebrush, the Valley now produces 80 per cent of that country's grapes, a third of its fruit and a quarter of its vegetables—in all, 220 crops.

Defences for a Sea-Pressed Land

On the 1st February 1953, under the onslaught of wind-whipped waves from the North Sea, dikes protecting the south-western Netherlands burst in 100 places. Some 400,000 acres were flooded and 1,800 people drowned.

The catastrophe, one of the worst in Dutch history, was a nation's ancient nightmare come true—for the Netherlands exists in the very maw of the sea, and the threat of a flood disaster is always present. A tiny country with the densest population in the world, the Netherlands has been adding to its own land since the 12th century by constructing an artificial coastline of dikes, then pumping out the impounded sea-water with windmills and electric pumps. Today fully half of the Netherlands, including the two largest cities, lies below the level of the sea. An altimeter at the Am-

(1) In 1956, work begins on a dike across a Netherlands estuary.

(2) Boats lay asphalt to hold down the sand at the dike's base.

(3) As a crowd cheers from the shore, the final concrete caisson

sterdam airport reads —13 feet; near Rotterdam it reads —30 feet.

The Netherlands' defences against the North Sea require constant maintenance by a corps of 10,000 engineers and workers. Day and night, 2,000 pumps and 400 windmills labour to keep the land dry. The Netherlands allots 8 per cent of its national budget for dike-building and upkeep.

In many places the dikes are battered and antiquated. After the 1953 flood, the Dutch government undertook a huge £235-million, 25-year construction programme to prevent any recurrence of the disaster. About 25 miles of new concrete dikes are being built across the mouths of estuaries in the south-west part of the country. These new barriers will form an outer wall to protect the vulnerable older dikes, and will shorten the coast-line of the Netherlands by 435 miles.

This project may keep the Dutch safe for many centuries, but it is not the end of their daring engineering ventures. One far-reaching scheme now being considered would pump 600,000 million cubic yards of earth into the interior of the country from the North Sea—and, by raising the sunken nation above the waves, end the threat of the sea for all time.

(4) A buffer of concrete is laid on both sides of the caisson core.

weighing 150 tons, is floated in to close the gap. It will be sunk with sand.

(5) The dike is completed after 65 months and topped by a road.

A ROUTE INTO A CONTINENT
Ships crowd a flight of locks on the Welland Canal of the St. Lawrence Seaway. These locks consisting of two massive steel gates 859 feet apart, can lift or lower a ship 138 feet. In the lifting process, the downstream gate is swung open and the other remains closed as the ship enters. Then the gates reverse position and water pours into the lock, slowly raising the ship.

LINK BETWEEN SEAS
Half hidden by dunes, an ocean liner makes the 100-mile run through the sea-level Suez Canal. The Canal was completed in 1869 after 10 years of work. A current runs through the Canal, carrying certain species of Red Sea fish into the Mediterranean Sea. Flourishing there, they now threaten extinction for some native fish species.

Man-Made Arteries for Commerce

Canals today bear more traffic then ever before—for the cheapest way to ship bulk cargo is still by water. The booming industrial sections of Germany, France, Belgium and the Netherlands depend on a 13,000-mile network of barge canals and rivers. The Great Lakes ports, benefiting from access to the Atlantic provided by the £540 million St. Lawrence Seaway, now handle 70 per cent as much cargo as all other U.S. ports combined.

The titans among canals are the lockless Suez—35 feet deep and 165 yards wide—and the six-lock Panama Canal. The Suez can provide a passage for 40 ships a day between the Mediterranean and the Red Sea. Traffic on the Panama waterway has reached 1,500 ships a month—and plans for a second canal across Central America are receiving attention.

Industry's Gargantuan Thirst

U.S. industry requires around 40,000 million gallons of water a day, about 25,000 million more than used in homes. About two-thirds of industrial water is used for cooling. One Celanese Corporation plant, e.g., uses 130,000 gallons of water a minute to cool petrochemical products. Water functions as a solvent in chrome-plating processes, and as a cleansing agent in the processing of coal. Water may also be the source of a product: magnesium is extracted from the sea (*left*). Water is used for mining: in the operation shown on the left below, super-heated water melts and forces sulphur out of the ground.

Many factories also employ water to carry off refuse (industrial waste is a common pollutant of rivers). On the other hand, some plants actually put polluted water to use. The Bethlehem Steel plant in Maryland uses 125 million gallons a day of effluent from Baltimore's sewage-treatment plant, cooling its hot steel with water that has already served the city.

MINING MAGNESIUM IN THE SEA
Practically all U.S. magnesium is chemically gleaned from sea water in the giant vats of a Texas plant. Sea water contains dissolved magnesium chloride, which is changed to magnesium hydroxide when lime is added. This is then processed to produce the light-weight metal.

MINING SULPHUR WITH WATER
In a technique employing water at 166°C. 1¾ million tons of sulphur are forced from the ground of Texas oil country each year. Pumped into the earth at extremely high pressure, the water liquefies the solid sulphur and helps to bear it up to the surface through an exit pipe.

COOLING MOLTEN STEEL
India's great Tata Works, situated 140 miles from Calcutta on the bank or a river, uses 4,500 gallons of water to process each ton of steel. The water, sprayed on the white-hot steel after it leaves the factory's blast furnaces, is recirculated and cooled for further use.

AN EXIT THROUGH THE DAM
A maintenance worker makes his way around an unused "scroll case" at the base of the dam. Connected to the up-river side of the dam by a tunnel, the scroll case encircles the horizontally positioned turbine wheel (*far right*), delivering water to the blades at a uniform velocity.

A swirling current races from the turbine at the

FIRST STEP TO ELECTRICITY
Two 12-foot steam turbine wheels are given a last-minute inspection at a General Electric plant in Schenectady, New York. The turbines installed in dams are far larger: their weight is measured in hundreds of tons, and the wheel casings are sometimes 65 feet across.

base of Wheeler Dam, part of the United States' Tennessee Valley Authority system. Cylinders at the back house the dam's generators.

Power from a Captive Torrent

One-fifth of the electric power used in the U.S. is generated by water held behind dams, and almost all the rest comes from water that is heated for steam generators. Hydroelectric dams work on a simple principle: the greater the vertical distance between water backed up behind a dam and the turbine blades at the base of the dam, the more the power generated. The turbines are connected by a drive shaft to a generator; some deliver as much as 300,000 horse-power to the electromagnets where current is produced. Hydroelectric projects are engineering monuments. But their construction is controversial. There is growing opposition from conservation groups in many parts of the world to power dams that provide electricity but destroy vast tracts of wild land, plants and animals.

A Dam to Draw Power from the Sea

Tides vary widely in different parts of the world. In a few places they run to extremes, with variations of 20 feet or more between high tide and low. This height difference, with its resulting water flow, is sufficiently great to be harnessed for the production of hydroelectric power. Construction began in 1961 on the world's first tidal-power dam, near the mouth of the Rance estuary on the coast of France. Twice a day, a tidal flow nearly equivalent to that of the river Mississippi thunders through the dam's 24 turbines and raises or lowers the water level 28 feet. The turbines are designed to generate 240,000 kilowatts of electricity when the tide is flowing in and the same amount when it is ebbing out. Because this amount is not always adequate to meet the region's power needs, the blades of the turbines—driven by electricity from near-by steam generators—can slowly pump water into the reservoir during periods of slack tide. The stored water can then be released to generate power at times of peak demand.

A GATEWAY FOR TIDAL ENERGY
The pump-turbine fixture above is the key to the Rance dam's versatility. It can drive a generator when the water flows through in either direction. It can also function as a motorized pump—its blades acting as a propeller to push water back into the reservoir when the tide is slack. The dam itself, hard by the city of St.-Malo, includes a lock (*far left*) for small boats.

8

Scarcity amidst Plenty

THIS ALKALINE DESERT, ONCE THE BED OF A LARGE LAKE, WAS CREATED WHEN THE LOS ANGELES WATER DEPARTMENT DIVERTED THE OWENS IN CENTRAL CALIFORNIA IN 1928.

In the 15th century, the once flourishing civilization of Arizona's Hohokam Indians vanished after the waters of their irrigation canals, fed by the river Salt, became so heavily salinized that they could no longer be used. More recently, in the most costly natural disaster in United States history, a four-year drought in the 1930s forced more than 500,000 Americans to flee the Dust Bowl States. In Brazil in 1954, and again in 1958, more than one million refugees from the drought-stricken northeast crowded into Rio de Janeiro and São Paulo, straining the cities' capacities to breaking point. In Tokyo in the summer of 1964, 41 dry days so reduced the water supply that tap water was available only part of every day, and in some sections residents had to line up at public stations for their daily ration. In Speyside, Scotland, there was a minor emergency in 1959 when drought dried up the streams that give Scotch whisky its distinctive flavour.

Water scarcities have plagued man throughout history and afflict him more than ever today. The need for water is increasing almost daily, as population and industry grow. Economic development, more than any other single factor, increases water use. In the underdeveloped nations, the *per capita* water consumption for all purposes—domestic, agricultural and industrial—is about 8 gallons a day. In the United States, it is about 1,500 gallons—of which about 1,400 are used for agriculture and industry. The world demand is expected to double before the end of the 20th century.

Does the world hold enough water to meet these needs? The answer is unequivocal. It does. When the earth was formed it held more than 8,000 million million tons of fresh water. It holds more than 8,000 million million tons today. Almost every drop that is used—whether for drinking, bathing, irrigating a desert or running an industrial plant—is eventually returned to the hydrologic cycle, draining to the sea, evaporating, and falling to earth as precipitation once again. Water is not used up. It is simply taken out of circulation for varying periods of time (with minor exceptions, such as the insignificant amount that is consumed chemically in some manufacturing processes).

But if the total supply of water is not a concern, its management and distribution are. People settle, and build factories and cities, where water is plentiful; then their cities and factories foul the water, converting sweet streams and lakes into open sewers and cesspools. Where nature is stingy, much money and ingenuity must be invested to guarantee sufficient water. The Aswan High Dam in Egypt, desalination plants in Israel and Kuwait, and the 240-mile-long aqueduct that serves Los Angeles are all efforts to compensate for local inadequacies.

A land that is naturally poor in water can escape total deprivation only by heroic effort. The newly established North African country of Mauritania is an extreme case. Mauritania achieved independence in 1960. Most of its 420,000-square-mile area lies within the Sahara. Its only sizeable sources of water are the river Senegal on the southern border, and the salt water of the Atlantic on its western shore. The capital city of Nouakchott, with about 50,000 inhabitants, uses water piped in from a well 40 miles away, and this is available for only eight hours a day.

The solution to Mauritania's water problem is still remote. One pilot desalination plant has been built there, but it will not supply enough fresh water to meet the nation's needs. Unless money and technical expertise are poured lavishly into the country, Mauritania seems doomed to remain a land of nomad herdsmen, wandering the desert from oasis to oasis in search of water for themselves and their cattle.

Making the desert flower

About 3,000 miles to the north-east lies Israel. Of its 8,000 square miles, only 1,200 are humid enough for non-irrigated agriculture. Compared to the river Ohio, the Jordan, Israel's main water source, is a creek. No rain falls during the summer months, and in half the land the annual precipitation is barely enough to keep the desert cactus alive. Yet since its establishment in 1948, Israel's population has trebled, and its industry and agriculture have kept pace with this increase. Pipelines bring fresh water into 98 per cent of Israel's homes. To date, nearly 90 per cent of the known water resources have been tapped. Millions of pounds, an advanced technology and strict controls are responsible for this seeming miracle.

Since 1950, the distribution and use of Israel's water supplies have been nationalized. Water is rationed to homes, industry and agriculture. Practically every drop of the sparse rainfall is saved: water tanks dot the roof-tops of Jerusalem, and in the farming areas the run-off ditches are lined to prevent seepage. One-quarter of Israel's electric power is used to pump up water from underground sources. In addition, two desalination plants purify water from the Gulf of Aqaba.

The knowledge that salt water can be made fresh is more than 2,000 years old. Sailors on long voyages have sometimes obtained their drinking water by placing pots of ocean water in the sun and trapping the condensed vapour. This same technique, in far more sophisticated form, is used in many desalination plants. In the so-called multistage flash-distillation process, sea water is heated and sprayed into a series of low-pressure chambers, where some of it vaporizes. As it passes through the chambers, more and more of the water evaporates, leaving behind more and more of the salt. At the end of the process, approximately one gallon of fresh water has been produced from every three and a half gallons of salt water.

Another technique of desalination reverses this procedure, freezing the water instead of evaporating it. Just as brine separates from steam when water evaporates, so it separates from ice crystals when water freezes. In the desalination process developed by the Israeli engineer Alexander Zarchin, chilled sea water is passed through a low-pressure chamber, which converts about half of it to ice. When the brine coating is removed, the ice can be melted into fresh water.

A third technique does not require changing the water either to steam or to ice. It cannot be used to desalinate sea water. But it is an efficient and economical way of treating brackish water. The city of Buckeye, Arizona, receives all its water from a plant that treats the output of near-by brackish wells by a process called electrodialysis. This technique makes use of the fact that when salt dissolves in water it separates into electrically charged atoms—negatively charged chloride and positively charged sodium. If salt water is introduced into a tank containing electrodes connected to a power source and surrounded by permeable membranes, the positive sodium will travel through one membrane to the negative electrode, and the negative chloride through the other membrane to the positive electrode. The water between the two membranes will therefore be free of salt.

The major problems associated with the desalination of sea water have less to do with its scientific aspects than with its cost. It takes considerable power to heat water sufficiently to convert it into steam, and only somewhat less to freeze it. And the smaller the capacity of the desalinating plant, the greater the cost of each gallon of fresh water produced. A multistage flash-distillation plant that provides water for Key West, Florida, delivers almost 2,500,000 gallons daily for 90 new pence per thousand gallons, compared with a cost of 15 new pence per gallons for water in Portland, Oregon.

Under certain circumstances, the development of very large-scale plants powered by nuclear energy might make desalination more practical. Such plants could both purify water and provide electrical power. A large nuclear plant proposed for Southern California is designed to produce 125 million gallons of fresh water a day at a cost ranging from 10 to 15 new pence per thousand gallons. The plant would also provide 1,800,000 kilowatts of electricity for the Los Angeles region.

But desalting the seas cannot provide a permanent solution for the water problems of the world. Nor, in much of the world, is a greater supply essential. The water is already there and available for use—if only society could decide how to use it. The future development of an entire region may hinge on the allotment of its water resources.

Taking water out of circulation

Industry and agriculture, the two main users of water, have very different effects on the available supply. Water used for agricultural irrigation is, for all practical purposes, consumed. Although it is eventually returned to the hydrologic cycle as rain, it is unlikely to fall back on the place from which it was taken. In the arid Middle East, this heavy drain on the water supply must be accepted if agriculture is to survive. But a country like the United States, which contains both arid and humid regions, has much greater freedom of choice. And a choice that is correct at one period in history may be questionable at another. For many years, government policy in the U.S. encouraged the development of agriculture in the dry South-West by offering water for irrigation at very low cost. When the policy was initiated, it was clearly in the national interest. It increased the agricultural yield and helped the South-West to grow. Phoenix, Arizona, which stands near the site of the drought-vanquished Hohokam civilization, owes its very existence to this policy. The original town of Phoenix, on the north side of the river Salt, was nearly wiped out in 1899, after a two-year dry spell. But after President Theodore Roosevelt pushed the National Reclamation Act through Congress in 1902, federal funds were available to build the Roosevelt Dam. In addition, Phoenix landowners contributed funds to repay the government and build irrigation and power projects. When the dam was completed, in 1911, the Salt River Valley had a population of about 12,000. Today three-quarters of a million people live in the area, which supplies the nation with about 2 per cent of its total cotton crop and nearly one-quarter of its lettuce.

But the expense of water now raises serious questions. In 1965, the United States put approximately 36 per cent of its water to work irrigating Western farmlands. According to a study conducted by Nathaniel Wollman of the University of New Mexico, such water would return five times as much money if it were used for recreation, and 60 to 80 times more if it were put to industrial use.

Nor is this situation exceptional. Industrial and domestic use of water always put less strain than agriculture on the supply. Water used for these purposes can be returned to the system quickly, and to a predetermined place. But its chemical composition is altered in the process of use, and it must be treated before it is used again. If it is dumped, untreated, into rivers and streams, the waters become polluted.

The menace of pollution

Water pollution inevitably produces economic and aesthetic problems, and may lead to health problems as well. Contaminated water can be a menace to life. Dysentery and typhoid fever are endemic in many parts of the underdeveloped world where primitive sanitary facilities permit sewage to enter drinking-water sources. In the industrialized nations, on the other hand, the treatment of drinking water is routine and water-borne diseases have been practically eliminated.

In any case, domestic wastes are present in the water of developed countries in much smaller volumes than industrial wastes—which may also be damaging. The complicated chemical compounds that form part of the wastes of certain advanced industrial processes are not always removed in water-treatment plants, and their long-term effects, both on stream life and on human health, are still unknown.

Some rivers contain nothing but used water: their total flow has been diverted for use and when the water is returned to the channel it is more or less polluted. According to Ernest P. Segasser of the New Jersey Pub-

PURIFYING SEWAGE before disposal is an essential step in preventing the pollution of rivers. The treatment process shown here is used at a factory in Poughkeepsie, New York. Raw sewage is first put through a comminutor —a device that pulverizes coarse debris. It is then mixed with bacteria-rich water in an aerator. As propeller blades agitate the mixture, the bacteria transform organic matter into harmless by-products. Heavy sludge is removed in a settling basin, after which the water is filtered through a mass of sand. At this point it is a clear liquid, which is chlorinated (to destroy any remaining bacteria) in the last tank. The treated sewage, now pure enough to drink, is finally piped into a creek that flows next to the factory.

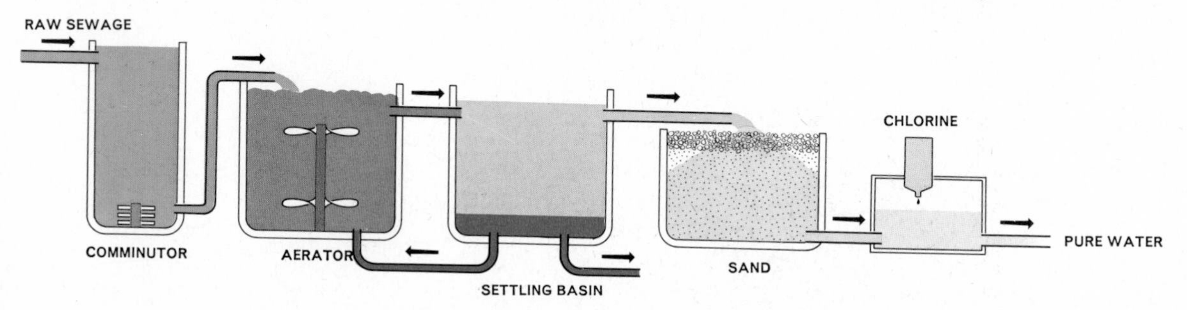

lic Health Department, two of his State's important streams can be described in precisely this way. "There have been periods," he wrote, "in which the flow in the Rockaway and Whippany Rivers consisted solely of waste water effluents." This description would apply equally to many of the smaller rivers in the United States during the low-flow periods of summer. Even a great river like the Hudson can contain considerable waste: of the used water dumped into it, only about 12 per cent has been thoroughly treated. Nor is the situation better in other lands. In Paris, the once sparkling Seine is murky and grey. In earlier days, a favourite London sport was fishing for salmon in the Thames. The sport is long since dead. The Thames is so dirty that salmon can no longer survive in it.

But all water contains some impurities. Even raindrops pick up dust and carbon dioxide as they fall. Because water accepts virtually every substance that comes into contact with it, it traps impurities of all sorts. And man has been using his rivers and lakes as waste-paper baskets since the dawn of history.

Flowing water: a self-purifying substance

Fresh water has the ability to absorb these wastes, transform them into useful or innocuous substances, and thus cleanse itself. Some of this self-purification is mechanical. The motion of the water stirs up the waste matter, dissolving some of it or breaking it into particles which either settle to the bottom or are diluted to harmlessness by incoming fresh water. In addition, a river or lake also metabolizes wastes, just as a living organism does. The river absorbs oxygen from the air and from water plants, which release it during the process of photosynthesis. The dissolved oxygen may act on organic wastes directly, by oxidation, "burning" them chemically so that nothing remains except carbon dioxide, water and a little ash. More often the oxygen operates indirectly, sustaining harmless bacteria that live in the water and consume sewage and other organic wastes, leaving behind an inoffensive residue that is either swept away, dissolved, or precipitated to the bottom of the stream.

But any body of water can suffer indigestion. If it is overloaded with wastes, it will exhaust its dissolved oxygen and be unable to purify any more foreign matter until it has taken in more oxygen from the air; and the amount of oxygen it can take in is limited by the fact that photosynthesis practically ceases at night. Decomposition of wastes, however, is a 24-hour process and a river loaded with additional refuse will never be able to catch up.

The organic pollution present in a river or lake can be determined by measuring the rate at which the dissolved oxygen is withdrawn from the water in the process of digesting wastes. First the polluted sample is mixed with water saturated with oxygen; the sample is sealed and kept for five days at a temperature of 20° C. Then the amount of dissolved oxygen in the sample is measured. The difference between the amount originally present and the amount present after five days indicates how much has been used in the digestive process. This biochemical oxygen demand, or BOD, is one standard measure of the amount of organic matter in the water. But it does not measure inorganic pollution. It is therefore not a measure of the potability of water. Even at a low BOD, water containing metallic wastes is not safe to drink.

Whenever a river's oxygen demand presses hard on its supply, the river is ailing. Excessive demand on the oxygen supply may result from eutrophication—a word meaning "burdened with nutrients". Nutrients added to a body of water have the same effect on its plant life as fertilizer has on a corn-field. The smallest forms of life—plankton, diatoms and algae—multiply rapidly. This changes the amount of dissolved oxygen available and upsets the natural balance of aquatic life. Fish that thrived at the original oxygen level begin to sicken and die, their places taken by species that require less oxygen and eat different foods. After a while, even these fish cannot get enough oxygen, and smother to death. If all the dissolved oxygen in the water is consumed, the only life it supports is bacteria that can decompose organic matter in the absence of oxygen—in the process releasing evil-smelling sulphide gases.

The major causes of eutrophication are nitrates and phosphates from sewage: some of these chemicals remain in the water even after treatment. If sewage is not treated at all, it is especially rich in nutrients. Agricultural fertilizers also contribute to eutrophication: they are often dissolved in rain and run-off water, and thus flow to rivers and lakes.

The treatment of water wastes

Only recently has the prevention of eutrophication been undertaken by the development of activated carbon units and special equipment that removes all the nitrates, phosphates and organic matter from sewage. The first commercial plant in the United States using this process was installed at Lake Tahoe, on the California-Nevada border. For treating less severe sewage problems, however, simple and efficient methods have long been available. In the activated-sludge method, which is widely used, the water is first held in a clarification unit, which permits some of its impurities to settle. Then, bacteria that feed on sewage solids are added and the entire mixture is agitated to increase the amount of dissolved oxygen and thus speed the digestive process. Finally, the water is again placed in tanks until the bacteria have settled. Although the effluent of a treatment plant is not potable, it is clear and sparkling. With the addition of chlorine, it becomes fit to drink.

The treatment of industrial wastes, which contain inorganic matter, is somewhat different. A metal-finishing plant, for example, can remove dissolved metals from its rinse waters by passing them through special filters, which exchange the harmful metallic products for harmless gas.

Whether or not waste water is pre-treated before it is dumped into a waterway, it must also be carefully processed in the next stage downstream, when it is taken out of the river for a water-supply system. First the solid wastes must be removed by alum or iron treatment. Then the water must be run through a series of fine-grained filters and disinfected with chlorine or some other chemical. Sometimes it must be softened with lime and soda ash. Afterwards, carbon dioxide must be added to ensure its chemical stability. Although this guarantees the water's safety, it does not guarantee its taste. In another section of his report, Segasser said of the New Jersey system served by the polluted streams: "There has never been any question of the potability of the water delivered, but its palatability is often questioned."

A triumph over pollution

That the water-pollution problem can be solved is evident from a look at the Ruhr Valley in Germany, where a remarkably effective antipollution programme has operated since 1913. In the Ruhr, five small rivers serve a population of about eight million people, inhabiting one of the most heavily industrialized regions in the world. The Ruhr Valley is the home of steel, chemical and pharmaceutical plants, which produce considerable waste water. Yet the water in some parts of the Valley is remarkably clear, and is much used by fishermen and swimmers. On a summer Sunday, as many as 40,000 Ruhr residents may be swimming in Lake Baldeney, one of the four large artificial lakes created by dams and built to purify the river's waters.

The Ruhr programme is carried out under the direction of a co-operative society; its members are 250 municipalities and 2,200 industrial companies interested in preventing river pollution before it can develop. Every member pays dues at a rate determined by the degree of pollution its used water shows: the cleaner the water, the lower the charge. This sliding scale encourages the members to purify their water before dumping it back into the river. The dues provide the society with money to finance regional water-purification and development programmes. Since 1948, the society has spent some £60 million on purification projects, building 110 water-treatment plants and carrying out research programmes that have enabled its members to improve their water-decontamination processes while economizing on over-all water use.

The record of the Ruhr Valley demonstrates how efficiently existing resources can be used. Yet even such frugality will not balance the world's water accounts. New supplies now untapped—or perhaps now unknown—must be made available if technological civilization is to continue its expansion. The study of these sources is one of the major tasks of the International Hydrological Decade, a project initiated in 1965 by the United Nations Educational, Scientific and Cultural Organization. More than 70 nations are co-operating in this 10-year programme which, by investigating a world-wide problem on a world-wide scale, will lay the scientific foundations that will in time enable man to meet his water needs.

The Diary of a Drink

Supplying modern cities with water is often a staggering task. According to recent figures, about 80 per cent of the U.S. population lives in towns and cities. The average U.S. city dweller needs about 125 gallons of water a day—a national total of 20,000 million gallons a day from 23,000 waterworks. This aggregate of municipal waterworks represents about £20 million in equipment and construction costs.

Few people stop to think what a varied life water leads on its way to the tap. Raw sewage, dissolved pollutants and silt must all be removed. The purification of drinking water is an ancient practice—a Sanskrit record dating from 2000 B.C. advises treating water by "boiling it and dipping a piece of hot copper into it seven times". Engineers now add chlorine to kill bacteria, and alum to precipitate out silt and other impurities. But new problems keep pace with advances in technology. Detergents accumulate in the water-table, and in some places tap water now foams with suds. Faced with ever-increasing consumption and a multiplicity of complex engineering problems, no city can be complacent about where its next drink is coming from.

A CHEMICAL CLEANSER

Machines in a water-purification plant at Cali, Colombia, chlorinate water before it enters the mains. Chlorination, introduced in the U.S. in 1908, kills off bacteria, including those of typhoid and dysentery. The chemical also reduces unpleasant tastes of dissolved organic compounds. The bad taste often attributed to chlorine actually occurs when not enough chlorine is added.

A NEW STYLE FOR STORAGE
Spheroid water tanks, with a total storage capacity of 625,000 gallons, stand 88½ feet high outside Carbondale, Illinois. The spheroid shape holds more water than an old-fashioned cylindrical tank that occupies the same space.

Urban Water in Short Supply

The critical New York City water shortage in the 1960s dramatically illustrated the difficulties of municipal water management: 18 reservoirs, as far distant as 125 miles, were all but drained by the North-East's longest drought. Water from the river Hudson was too polluted to tap (a purification plant built in an earlier drought had been deemed unnecessary and closed down). Only strict conservation kept city taps from going dry.

Water shortages are increasingly common. In 1964, when Denver's soaring population grew too great for the city's existing reservoirs, engineers had to blast a 23-mile tunnel under the continental divide and divert a river 40 miles away. As consumption rose in Carbondale, Illinois, the city had to build huge water tanks (*left*) that could be pumped full each night. Some cities, however, were far-sighted: in 1915, Portland, Oregon, planned a water supply system big enough for 10 times its population and capable of expansion.

REFILLING A DISTANT RIVER
A modern water system often assumes extraordinary complexity. Denver built this dam on the Williams Fork river—100 miles from the city, and on the opposite side of the continental divide—not to supply water to the city, but to replenish the river Colorado, which does.

TAP-WATER IN RESERVE
Storage ponds in a park overlooking Portland, Oregon, are part of the city's extensive reservoir system (including 8 lakes, close to 60 tanks and 6 basins). Getting the water to Portland is easy: the city is amply supplied by a watershed at the base of near-by Mount Hood.

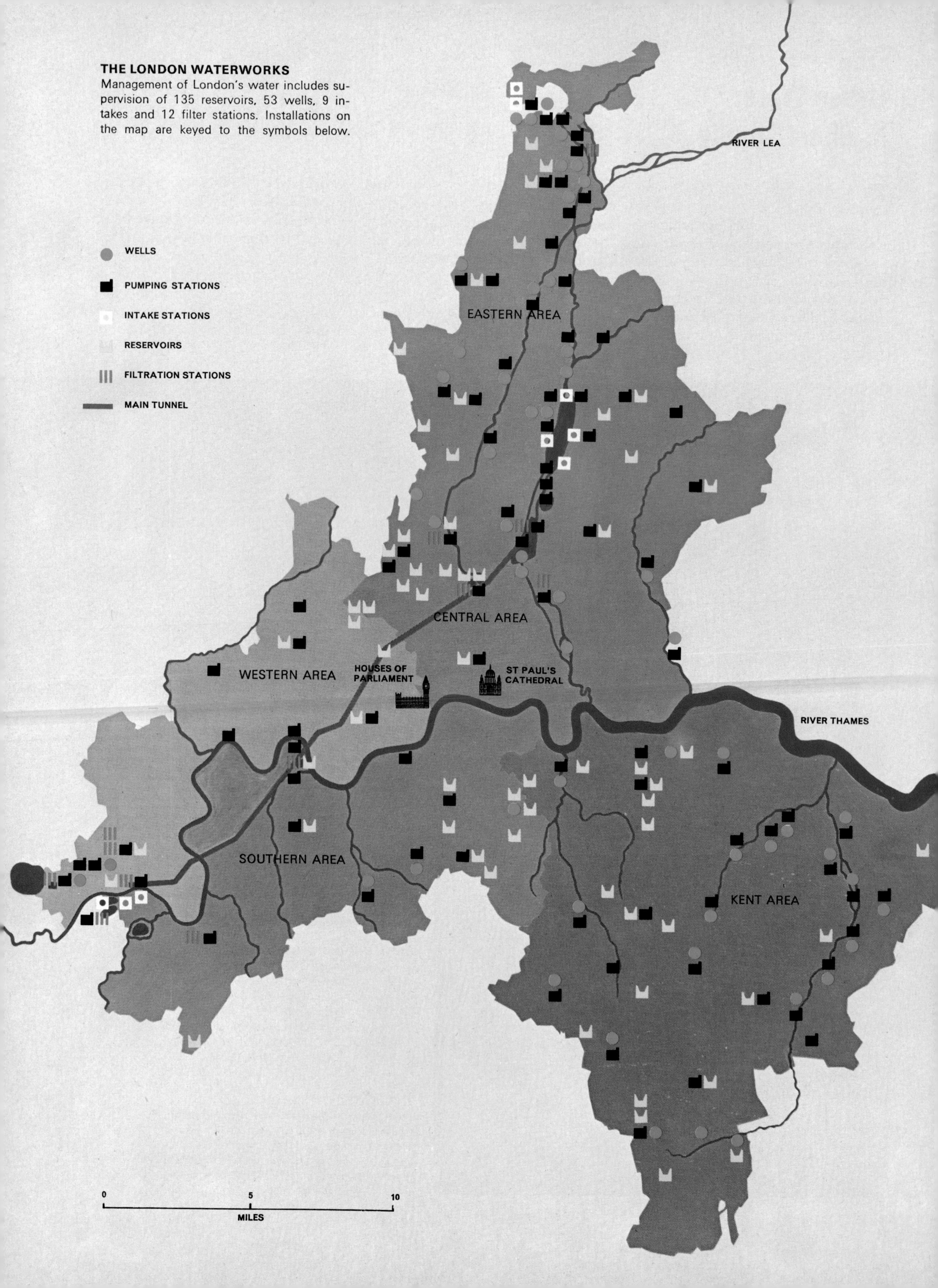
THE LONDON WATERWORKS
Management of London's water includes supervision of 135 reservoirs, 53 wells, 9 intakes and 12 filter stations. Installations on the map are keyed to the symbols below.
WELLS
PUMPING STATIONS
INTAKE STATIONS
RESERVOIRS
FILTRATION STATIONS
MAIN TUNNEL
RIVER LEA
EASTERN AREA
CENTRAL AREA
WESTERN AREA
HOUSES OF PARLIAMENT
ST PAUL'S CATHEDRAL
RIVER THAMES
SOUTHERN AREA
KENT AREA
0
5
10
MILES

A Maze of Water Mains

Water is supplied to London, England (a 616-square-mile city with a population of eight million), through a gargantuan underground tangle of pipes built up over seven centuries. There are nearly 10,000 miles of pipe under the London streets—a mileage more than double that of the streets themselves—delivering over 340 million gallons of water a day, mostly from the river Thames.

The construction of this system began in 1237, when King Henry III had lead pipes installed. Wooden and stone conduits soon expanded service. In the centuries that followed, a succession of private companies laid additional pipes under the city, keeping vague records and often duplicating one another's service.

In 1904, city engineers finally took charge of the system (the last private company became part of the Greater London Council in the 1960s) and began to unravel the fantastic snarl of unmapped mains and leaky pipes. They repaired and replaced miles of pipe, installed new equipment and built new reservoirs. Tangles of antiquated pipe had to be entirely bypassed with new mains. The engineers now have the system in hand—although they are still tracing leaks to pipes that no one knew existed.

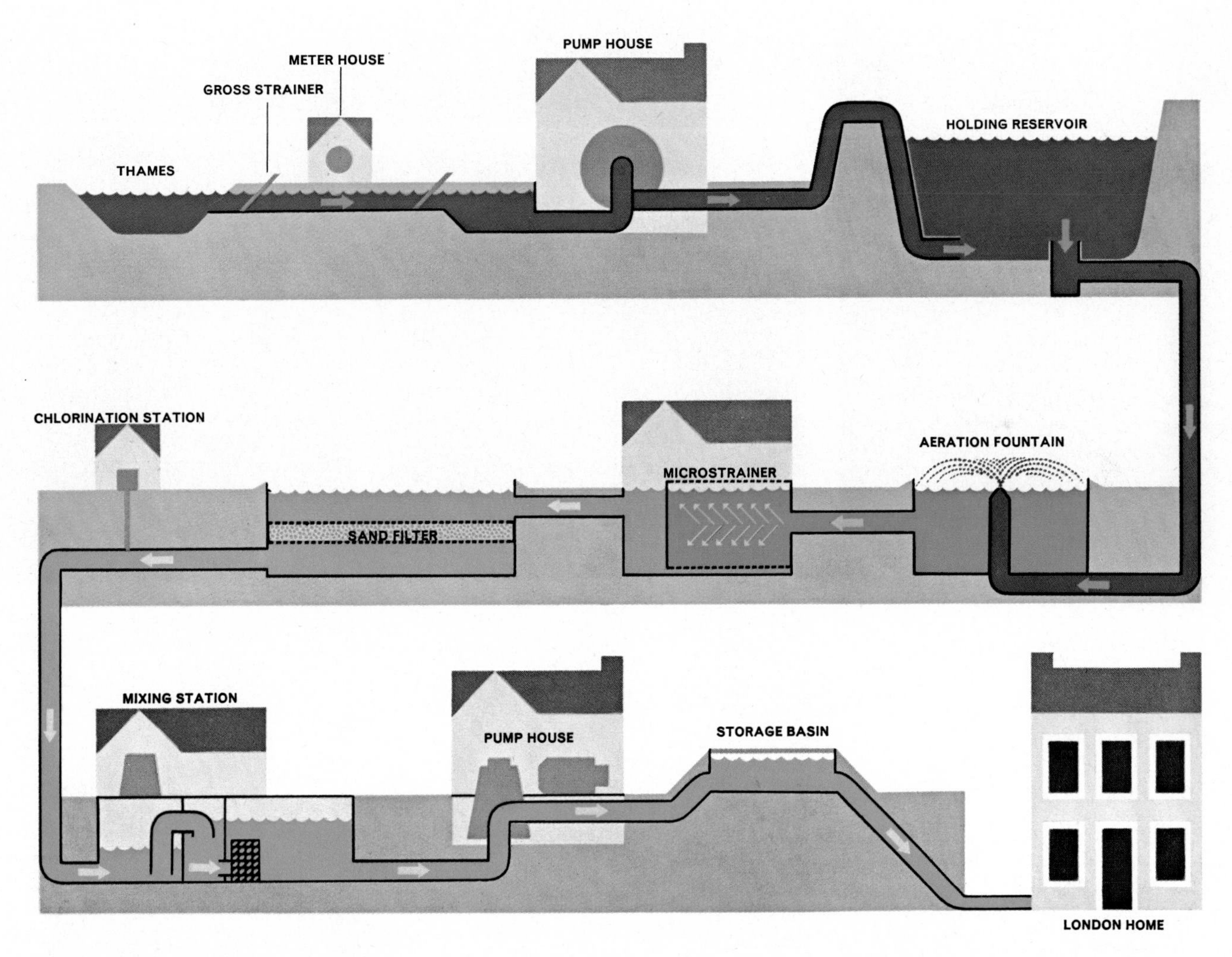

RELAY STATIONS FOR CITY WATER
London's water, drawn from the Thames, is sent through a sequence of processing plants, shown schematically above from top left to bottom right. Water from the river first passes through a coarse strainer that removes bulk waste. It then flows through a meter house, where its volume and rate of flow are recorded. At a pumping station it is forced up into a holding reservoir. From there it flows down into an aeration fountain (aeration oxidizes many impurities). Next it flows through a fine-mesh microstrainer that filters out mud and silt, and a sand filter that removes most of the remaining impurities. Chlorine (which kills micro-organisms) is then added into the main, and the treated water goes through a mixing station. Finally, the water is pumped into a storage reservoir, from which it is piped into homes.

MEASURING THE INTAKE

A 10-foot-wide main brings water into Baltimore's Ashburton plant. A thin pipe connects a narrow segment of the main (*centre*) to a measuring device. By checking the rate of flow, engineers can keep track of the drain on reservoirs and adjust dosages of purification chemicals. About 85 million gallons a day (one-third of the city's water) are processed here.

CLEANING CLOUDY WATER

A conveyer belt dumps alum, an aluminium compound, into untreated water. Mud particles which cloud water stick to the alum and are settled out, a process known as "flocculation".

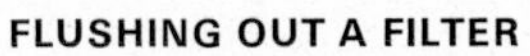

FLUSHING OUT A FILTER

In a daily cleansing operation, water is forced up through one of 20 identical 2,100-square-foot sand filters in the Baltimore plant. The slimy residue spills over into troughs that carry it away to a waste reservoir. When the filter is in use, water seeps down through 34 inches of sand, gravel and stones, after which it is crystal-clear and needs only to be chlorinated.

Making the Water Fit to Drink

The impurities in a city's water supply must either be removed by filtration, precipitated out, or chemically neutralized. Baltimore's water, processed in the £5½-million Ashburton plant pictured here, contains only a moderate amount of suspended materials—about three parts per one million parts of water (Kansas City, in contrast, must purify water with 800 parts per million). But after it is treated, Baltimore's water contains less than one part per 10 million—a trace detectable only by the most sensitive instruments.

The Ashburton plant's nerve centre is a laboratory where chemists, on duty around the clock, test water piped from every part of the plant. They can instantly spot a bad filter or settling tank, and can quickly prescribe antidotes for fluctuations in impurities. A heavy thunderstorm, for instance, can cause a sudden increase in silt; adding more alum makes the silt settle. Typhoid bacteria increase during the summer, and extra chlorine must be added. During an average year, the plant removes about 27,000 tons of impurities from the water—enough to clog up every main and tap in the city.

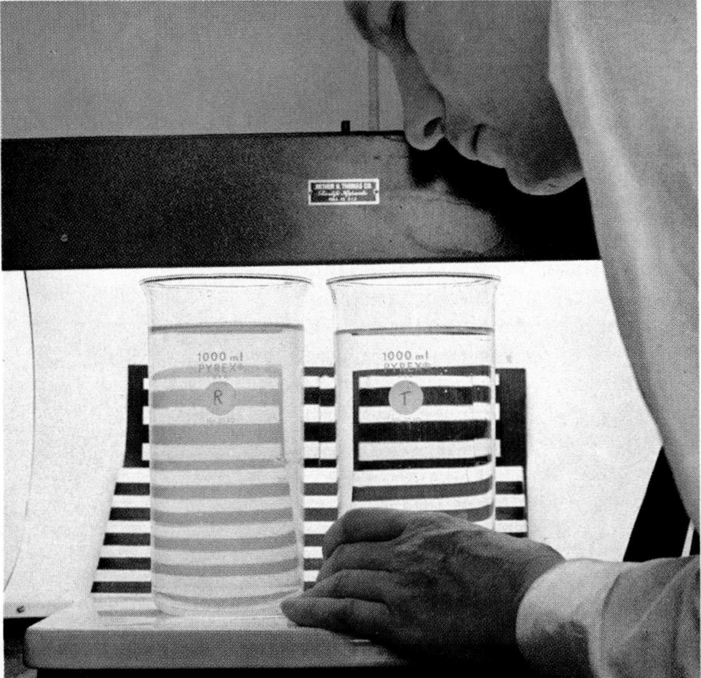

BEFORE AND AFTER
A chemist compares the clarity of raw and treated water, studying the samples against a black-lined light table. The degree to which the black lines are obscured is an indication of how much material is suspended in the water, and how much alum must be added to remove it. The sample of treated water has had 99.9 per cent of the impurities removed from it.

First in a series of experimental desalination plants underwritten by the Federal government, this installation at Freeport, Texas, was built in

Fresh Water for Freeport

Freeport, Texas, with a population of 11,800, was a city in search of water when, in 1958, the U.S. government decided to build an experimental desalting plant along the Gulf Coast. About 30 cities applied for the plant; Freeport, where even local well water was salty, was selected.

At a cost of £500,000 the plant above was erected to distil sea water under reduced pressures in long vertical tubes. This design was later modified to add a second stage of desalination by the flash distillation process, which uses extremely low pressures to cause the water to boil, or "flash", almost instantaneously while leaving salt behind. These methods are so efficient that at Freeport, for instance, the fresh water produced had too little salt in it—and people complained that it tasted flat. To remedy the situation, the distilled water had to be mixed with salty water from local wells, so that some of its taste could be restored.

Experts predict that within 20 years plants at critical spots will be producing 400 million gallons a day, enough to supply the largest cities.

DISTILLING THE SEA

When superheated water enters a chamber at reduced pressure, the water flashes into steam. This is the basis of flash distillation, the desalting process illustrated on the right. Sea water first enters the system (*left centre*) in a pipe which forms coils as it passes through successive evaporating chambers. The pipe carries the water past a furnace where it is superheated to 120° C. As the water flows into and through the evaporators, each of the chambers is filled with steam. New supplies of sea water keep the coils cool, and the steam condenses on them and drips into drains that lead to storage tanks. A briny residue (*dark red*) is left behind.

1961 to provide the city and near-by industries with a million gallons of fresh water a day. It draws its supply from the Gulf of Mexico.

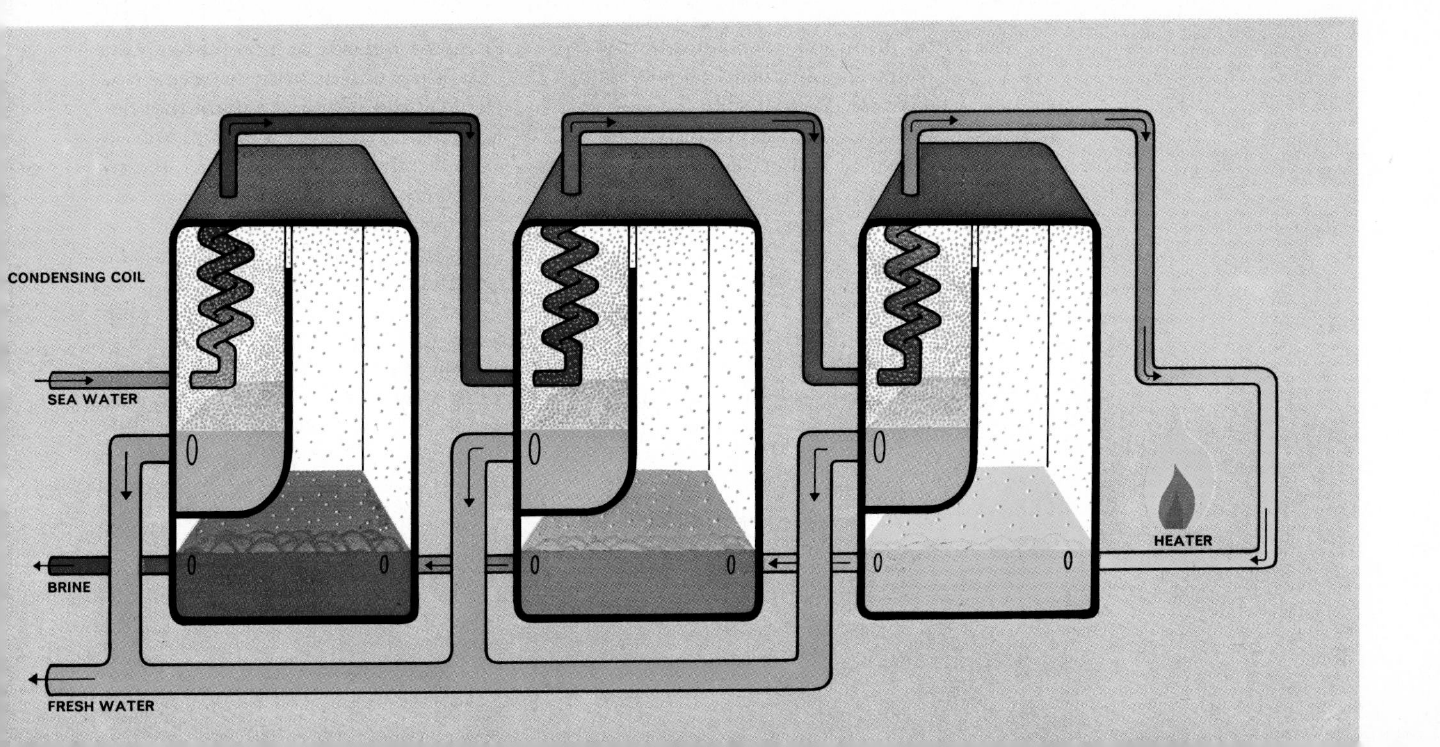

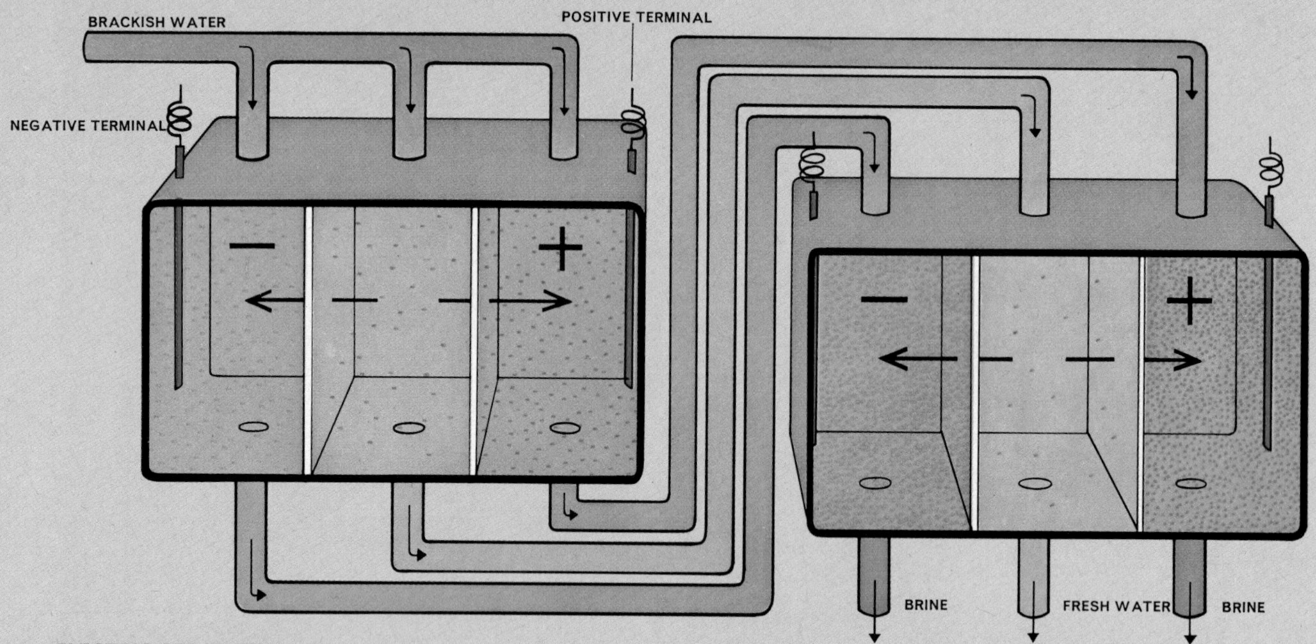

ELECTRIC SEPARATION
In electrodialysis, salt water is pumped through a series of electrified containers, each of which is divided into three compartments by thin membranes almost impermeable to water. When salt dissolves in water it breaks up into electrically charged particles, or ions, of sodium and chlorine. The sodium ions, which carry a positive charge, pass through the membranes and cluster around the negative terminal; the negatively charged chlorine ions are attracted to the positive terminal. The process is repeated until the centre chamber is free of ions.

Drinking Sea Water

Scientists have thought up dozens of different schemes for removing the salt from sea water, although none has yet proved more efficient than the distillation methods employed at Freeport, Texas.

The 4,083 inhabitants of Symi, an island near Greece, get all their water from one solar-distillation unit which supplies nearly 3,500 gallons a day. At Wrightsville Beach, North Carolina (testing ground for the U.S. Office of Saline Water), a freezing plant produced 170,000 gallons of desalted water a day. Two other methods have shown promise and are being tested: one, called reverse osmosis, desalts water by passing it through a synthetic membrane; another, called hydration, involves the addition of propane to salt water. The propane forms a solid compound with the water, which is then freed when the compound is heated. However, scientists have yet to discover an efficient membrane for osmosis or to design an efficient plant for hydration.

Where the water is not excessively salty, still another method can be used. In Webster, South Dakota, the local water was distastefully brackish (almost twice as salty as the government regards as acceptable) but only a fraction as briny as ocean water. Webster installed a plant that desalinates its water by a process known as electrodialysis (*above*), which is prohibitively expensive except where the salt problem is not great. The Webster plant produces about 200,000 gallons of water a day.

Large-scale desalination may pose some unexpected problems. Desalting enough sea water to supply New York City for a year, for instance, would produce a briny effluent with about 55 million tons of salt—more than is used in the U.S. in two years.

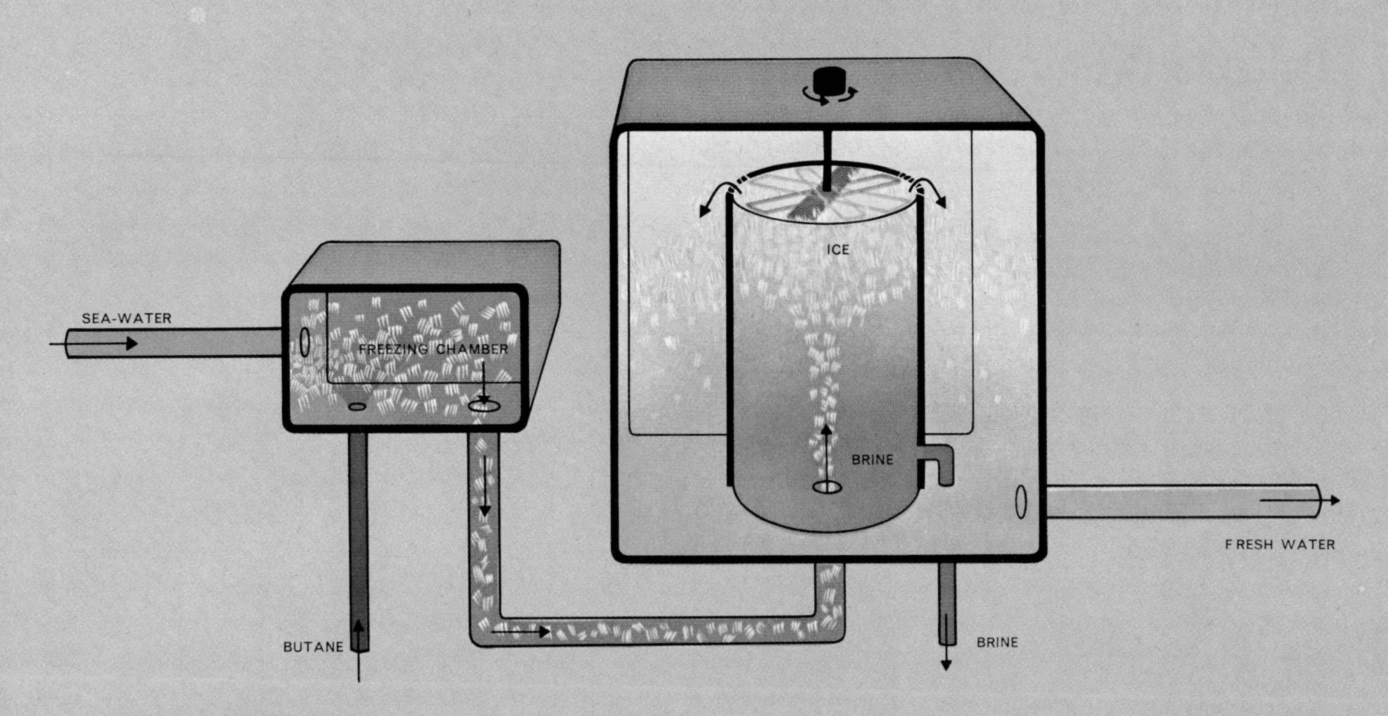

FREEZING OUT SALT

One promising method of separating salt from water is freezing the salt water: the salt is left behind as pure ice is formed. In the procedure shown here, supercooled butane is pumped into salt water in a freezing chamber. An icy slush is formed, and is pumped into the bottom of a large separating vat. The ice particles float to the surface of the vat, and are scraped off the top by a rotating blade. The ice spills over into the surrounding chamber, melts into pure water and is piped away. Waste brine is drained at the bottom of the vat.

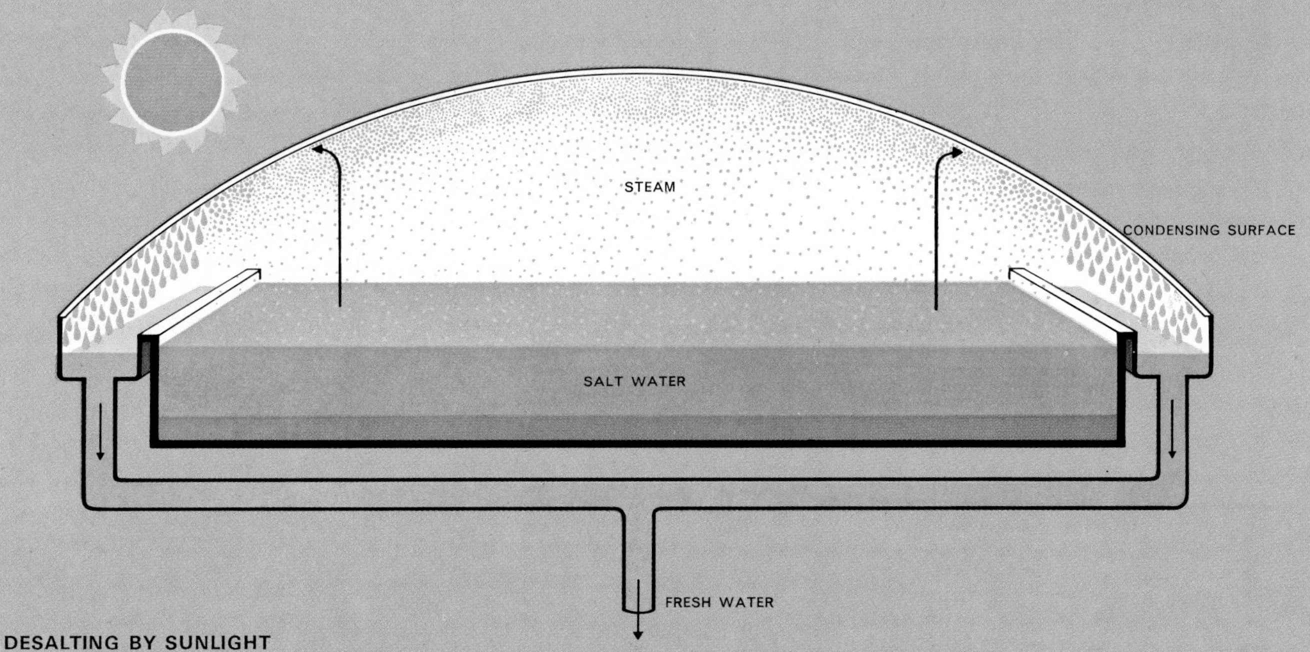

DESALTING BY SUNLIGHT

Solar distillation uses the sun's energy to desalt brine. Salt water is piped into a flat trough enclosed under a transparent plastic dome. The sun's heat causes the water to evaporate, forming a pure vapour which recondenses on the underside of the dome. This pure water trickles down the dome, drips into collecting troughs at the edges of the unit and is drained out. The briny residue left behind is flushed away. This method is inexpensive but impractical in many cases because the yield is low: at best 0.11 gallon per square foot of basin area per day.

Spot-Checking Polluted Rivers

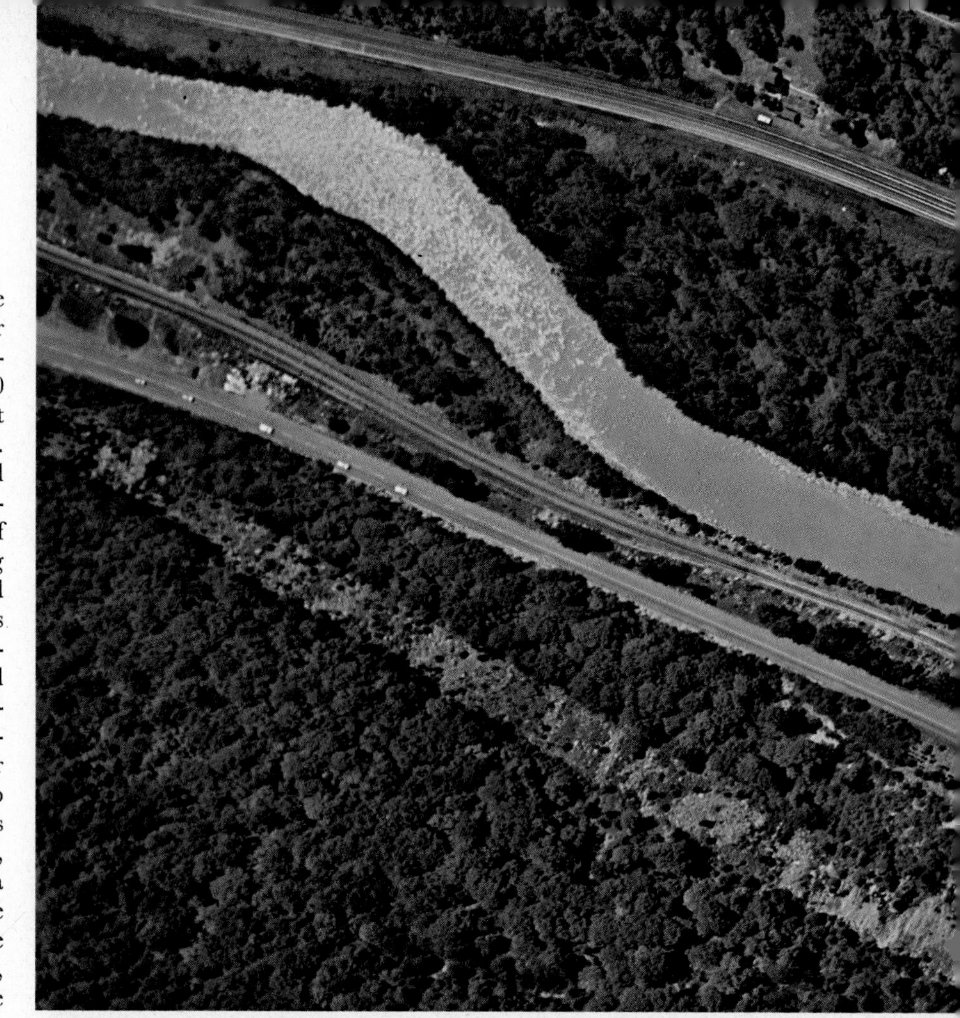

The pollution of rivers is one of the major factors now limiting the water supplies of many cities. Urban populations daily produce about 100 gallons of waste per capita, and most of this sewage is flushed into rivers. In addition the waters are polluted with industrial oils, corrosive chemicals, acids, dyes and the like. One of the newest techniques for studying this problem is the use of infra-red photography, illustrated here. This tool has been employed by hydrologists for only about two years, and its potential has not been completely explored. But it is clear that infra-red film, which reacts to heat rather than light, can sometimes show up pollution where ordinary film does not. In the photograph at the top, brown sewage can be seen polluting a dark-green river, mixing with the water as it moves downstream. In the infra-red photograph at the bottom, the same process shows up as a change from blue water to white. Where the pollutant has not visibly discoloured the river, infra-red photography may give scientists their first clue to the existence of a foreign substance in the water. Making photographic surveys from the air, scientists can do in an hour or two what might otherwise take 10 days. The resultant photographs do not indicate what is polluting the water (that requires laboratory analysis), but they suggest where water samples should be collected.

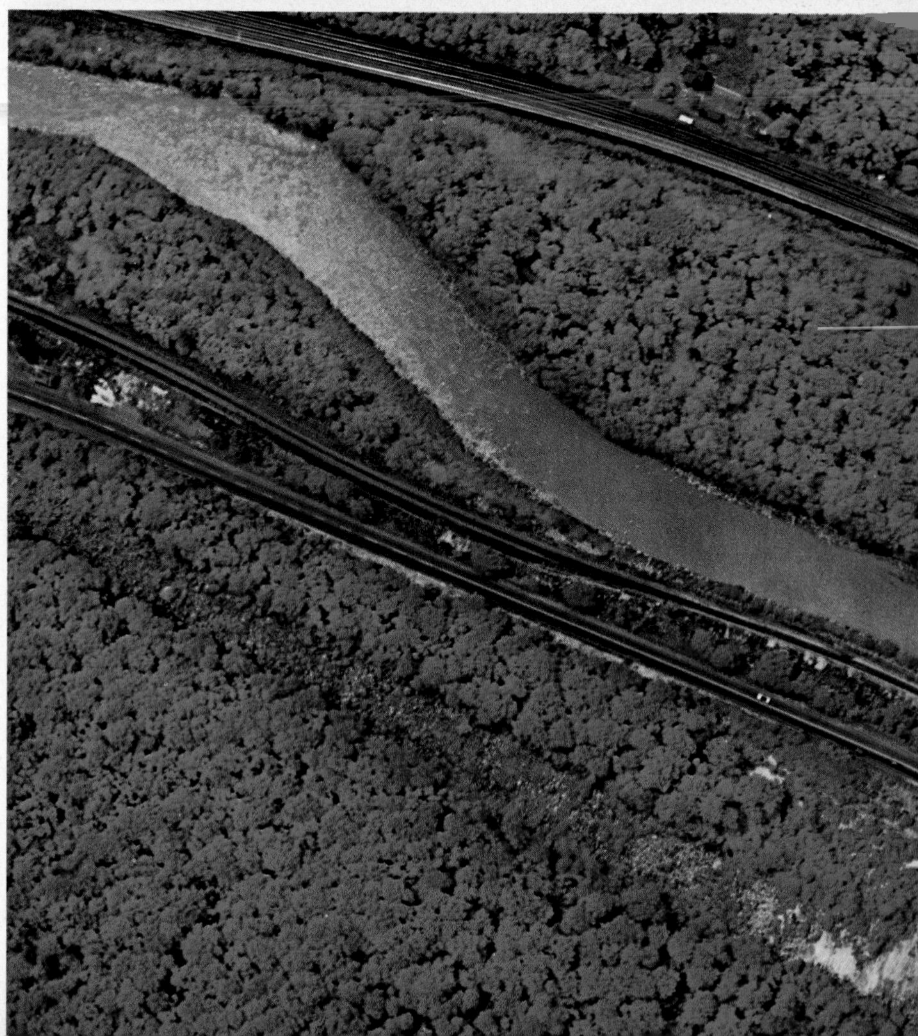

TWO VIEWS OF POLLUTION
Effluent from the circular waste tanks of a factory enters the centre of a river through two pipes (*far right*), as seen in both colour and infra-red photographs. Since most pollutants reduce the oxygen supply of the water, the degree of pollution can be measured by changes in the river's dissolved oxygen content. Above the plant, there are about five parts of dissolved oxygen per million of water. Below the plant, and for 10 to 20 miles downstream, the dissolved oxygen value is reduced nearly to zero.

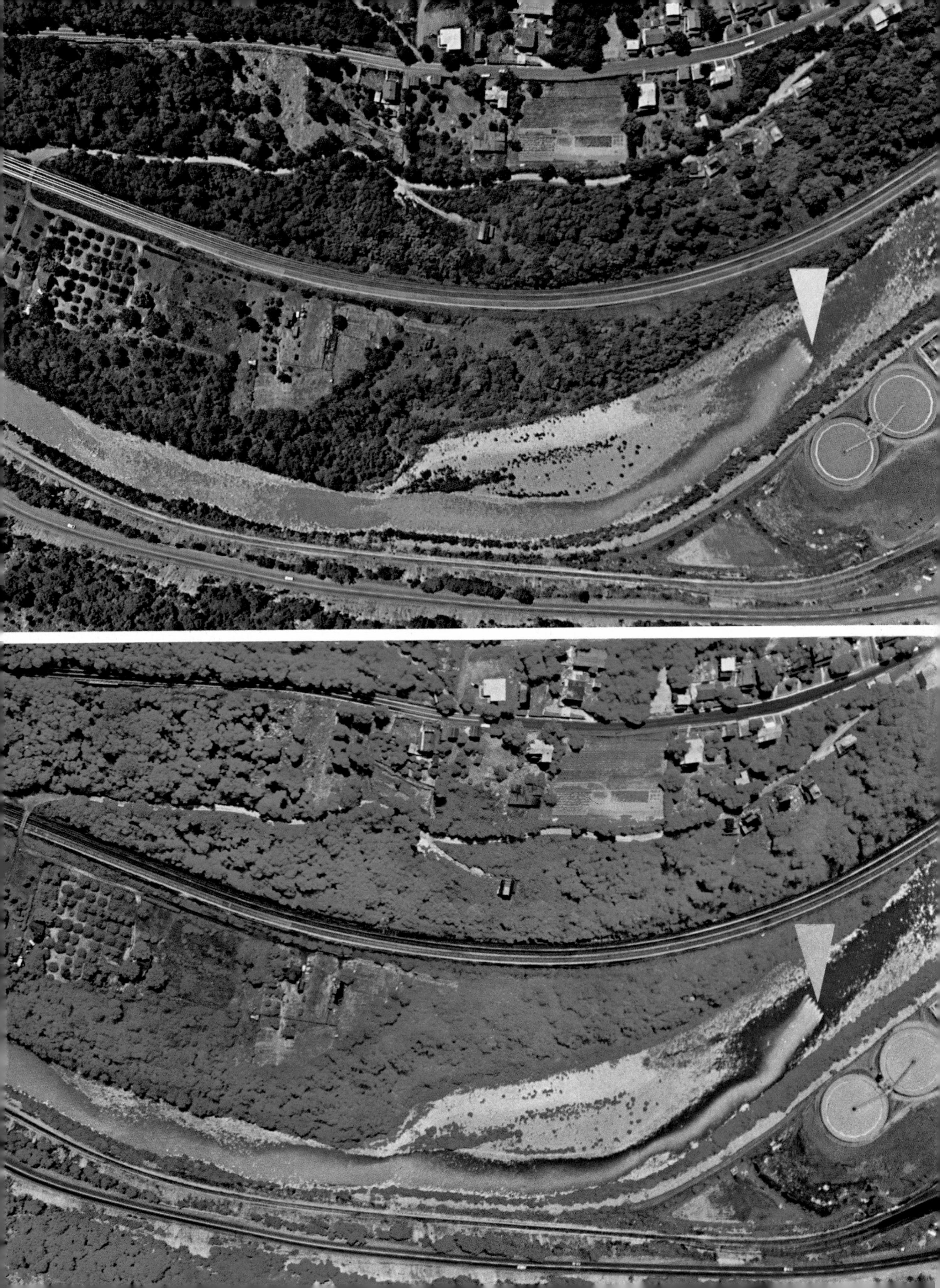

The Dictionary of the Hydrologist

A FAULT can discharge juvenile water; an oxbow is not subject to underflow. This may sound like gibberish, but it is in fact a stringing together of common hydrological terms (though perhaps in a way no hydrologist would use them). This science, like most others, has a language all its own. Mixed in with such technical terms as "piezometric surface" and "zone of aeration" are other, seemingly familiar words that take on different meanings to the hydrologist. Here is a glossary of water words, most of which appear in this book.

WATER EQUIVALENTS

1 cubic foot of water = 6¼ gallons
1 cubic foot per second (c.f.s.) = 375 gallons per minute
1 c.f.s. day = 1 cubic foot per second flowing for 1 day = about 2 acre feet
1 acre foot = 1 acre covered to a depth of 1 foot = 43,560 cubic feet or 269,542 gallons
1 gallon of water = 10 pounds
1 ton of water = 224 gallons

ANNUAL FLOOD The highest flow a river normally reaches during the year. This point is not usually a flood in the ordinary meaning, since there is no overflow.

AQUIFER. A layer of rock, sand or gravel through which water can pass (see PERMEABILITY).

ARTESIAN. Describes underground water trapped under pressure between layers of impermeable rock. An artesian well is one that taps artesian water.

CAPILLARITY. The force that causes water to rise in a constricted space through molecular attraction, often against the pull of gravity.

CONDENSATION. The transformation of water from a vapour to a liquid, such as occurs when vapour in the atmosphere is changed to droplets of rain.

CONE OF DEPRESSION. A conical dimple in the water table surrounding a well, caused by pumping. The faster water is pumped, the deeper and steeper the cone becomes.

CONSUMPTIVE USE The use of water, especially in irrigation, in such a way that it is converted to vapour and returned to the atmosphere. Thus it can no longer be directly returned to the stream or underground source from which it originated.

DESALINATION. The process of removing salt from water. Most often it is a distillation process, in which salt water is evaporated, then condensed, leaving the salt as residue.

DISCHARGE. The rate of flow of surface or underground water, generally expressed in cubic feet per second. It also refers to the emptying of a river into a lake or ocean.

DRAINAGE BASIN. The geographical area within which all surface water tends to flow into a single river or stream via its tributaries.

EROSION. The wearing down of the earth's surface by water.

EVAPORATION. The transformation of water into a vapour. This physical change occurs when heat is absorbed by the liquid, as when boiling water turns to steam.

EVAPOTRANSPIRATION. The process by which water, evaporated from the earth and given off by plants and animals, is returned to the atmosphere as vapour.

FAULT. A break in the earth's crust, causing a slippage and displacement of layers of the crust. The fault may raise a layer of rock anywhere from a few inches to thousands of feet higher than the adjoining layers. This affects both the location and flow of the underground water, often causing springs to appear.

FLOOD-PLAIN. A strip of flat land bordering a stream or river, consisting of sediment laid down over the centuries by the river when it moves laterally within the valley walls and is subject to overflow during high floods.

GEOMORPHOLOGY. The study of the earth's form and its evolution, both of which owe much to the action of water in rivers and glaciers.

GEYSER. From an Icelandic word meaning "Gusher". A natural fountain of ground-water, forced to the surface by steam at fairly regular intervals. Geysers occur when water deep in the earth is converted to steam by hot volcanic rock. Steam pressure then builds up against the water on top of it; this produces a spectacular eruption, after which the geyser subsides until steam pressure builds up enough to set it off again.

GROUND-WATER. The term describing all subsurface water. It can be found as deep as several miles.

HEADWATER. The beginning of a stream or river, its source or its upstream portion.

HYDROLOGIC CYCLE. The process by which water constantly circulates from the sea to the atmosphere to the earth, and back to the sea again.

HYDROLOGY. The scientific study of the water found on the earth's surface, in its subsurface and in the atmosphere.

HYDROLYSIS. The process by which a compound reacts chemically with water and forms new substances. For example, ferric chloride, when placed in water, forms some molecules of both hydrochloric acid and ferric hydroxide.

INFILTRATION. The method by which surface water is soaked into the ground through tiny openings in the soil.

JUVENILE WATER. Water that has been trapped for ages far below the earth's surface, so that it cannot take part in the hydrologic cycle.

LEACHING. The process by which water, seeping through earth and rocks, dissolves and carries away certain minerals or compounds, such as the oxides of iron.

OXBOW. A curved lake, created when a bend is abandoned by a river that has changed its course.

PERMEABILITY. The capacity of a solid to allow the passage of a liquid. The permeability of dirt or rock is determined by the number of pores, or openings, their size and shape, and the number of interconnections between them.

PIEZOMETRIC SURFACE. The theoretical level to which water should rise under its own pressure if tapped by a well or spring; the water level of an artesian well is one point on such a surface.

POROSITY. The ability of rock and other earth materials to hold water in open spaces or pores; the percentage of such open space in relation to total volume.

PRECIPITATION. The discharge of condensed water vapour by the atmosphere in the form of rain, hail, sleet or snow.

RIFFLE: A rock or gravel bar in a stream over which backed-up water runs at greater than normal speed during periods of low flow. Riffles tend to occur at relatively uniform intervals along most streams.

SALTS. A group of soluble compounds, including sodium chloride—common table salt—dissolved from earth and rocks by the water that flows through them (see LEACHING).

SEDIMENT. Tiny particles of dirt and rock carried by water, which eventually settle to the bottom.

SPRING An opening in the surface of the earth from which ground-water flows.

STREAM ORDER. The method by which river systems are ranked in size and complexity. Streams of the first order include spring-, rain- or snow-fed brooklets without tributaries; streams of the second order are fed by those of the first order, and so on. A great river such as the Mississippi may have a stream order as high as 10.

TERRACE. A plateau on the side of a valley, representing an old flood-plain no longer reached by the river below.

TRANSPIRATION. The exhalation of water vapour by the leaves of plants.

TSUNAMI. This Japanese word meaning "storm wave" refers to a giant ocean wave produced by a siesmic disturbance beneath the ocean floor. The wave is sometimes mistakenly called a tidal wave, which actually results from the pull of the sun and moon.

TURBIDITY. Cloudiness caused by sediment suspended in water. Rivers are generally at their most turbid following a rainstorm, when extraordinary amounts of sediment carried into the stream by the run-off have not yet settled.

UNDERFLOW. The downstream movement of ground-water through permeable rock beneath a river-bed.

WATER-TABLE. The level to which ground-water rises, or the surface of the zone of saturation.

WITHDRAWAL USE. The use of surface or underground water that is later returned to the hydrologic cycle, although not necessarily to the same place. An example is most water piped into homes and industrial plants.

ZONE OF AERATION. The layer of the earth, above the water-table, containing air-filled spaces through which water seeps.

ZONE OF SATURATION. The layer beneath the zone of aeration, in which all openings are filled with ground-water. The water-table is the top of the zone of saturation.

FURTHER READING

General

Bardach, John, *Downstream: A Natural History of the River.* Harper & Row, 1964.

Collis, John Stewart, *The Moving Waters.* William Sloane Associates, 1955.

†Davis, Kenneth S., and John Arthur Day, *Water, The Mirror of Science.* Heinemann Educ., 1964.

King, Thomson, *Water, Miracle of Nature.* Collier-Macmillan, 1953.

Leopold, Luna B., and Walter B. Langbein, *A Primer on Water.* U.S. Government Printing Office, 1960.

Water Resources Council, *Nation's Water Resources, First National Assessment of Water Resources Council.* U.S. Government Printing Office, 1968.

Earth Sciences

†Dury, G. H., *The Face of the Earth.* Penguin, 1959.

Flint, Richard Foster, *Glacial and Pleistocene Geology.* Wiley, 1957.

†Kuenen, P. H., *Realms of Water.* Wiley, 1963.

Leet, L. D., and Sheldon Judson, *Physical Geology.* Prentice-Hall, 1965.

Leopold, Luna B. and Walter B. Langbein, "River Meanders". *Scientific American,* June 1966.

Leopold, Luna B., M. Gordon Wolman and John P. Miller, *Fluvial Processes in Geomorphology.* W. H. Freeman, 1964.

Longwell, Chester R., and Richard F. Flint, *Introduction to Physical Geology.* Wiley, 1962.

McGuinness, C. L., *The Role of Ground Water in the National Water Situation.* Water Supply Paper 1800, U.S. Government Printing Office, 1963.

†Meinzer, Oscar E., *Hydrology.* Dover: Constable, 1942.

Strahler, Arthur, *The Earth Sciences.* Harper & Row, 1963.

Thornbury, William D., *Regional Geomorphology of the United States.* Wiley, 1965.

Wright, H. E. Jr., and Davis G. Frey, eds., *The Quaternary of the United States.* Princeton University Press, 1965.

History

Boumphrey, Geoffrey, *Engines and How They Work.* Vista, 1960.

Brittain, Robert, *Rivers, Man and Myths.* Longmans, 1958.

De Camp, L. Sprague, *The Ancient Engineers.* Souvenir, 1963.

Derry, T. K., and Trevor Williams. *A Short History of Technology.* Oxford University Press, 1961.

Kirby, Richard Shelton, et al., *Engineering in History.* McGraw-Hill, 1956.

Waters of Life

*Ray, Peter M., *The Living Plant.* Holt, Rinehart and Winston, 1963.

*Schmidt-Nielsen, Knut, *Animal Physiology.* Prentice-Hall, 1964.

Wald, George, "The Origin of Life." *Scientific American,* August 1954: W. H. Freeman.

Wolf, A. V., "Body Water." *Scientific American,* November 1958.

Problems, Uses and Management

Davis, Kenneth S., *River on the Rampage.* Doubleday, 1953.

Grava, Sigurd, *Urban Planning Aspects of Water Pollution Control.* Columbia University Press, 1969.

Hoyt, William G., and Walter B. Langbein, *Floods.* Princeton University Press, 1955.

Kneese, Allen V., "New Directions in Water Management." *Bulletin of the Atomic Scientists,* May 1965.

Langbein, Walter B., and William G. Hoyt, *Water Facts for the Nation's Future.* Ronald Press, 1959.

Leopold, Luna B., and Thomas Maddock Jr., *The Flood Control Controversy.* Ronald Press, 1954.

Maxon, James, *Volta, Man's Greatest Lake,* Praeger, 1969.

Moss, Frank E., *The Water Crisis,* Praeger, 1969.

Nadeau, Remi, *The Water Seekers.* Doubleday, 1950.

Swenson, H. A., and H. L. Baldwin, *A Primer on Water Quality.* U.S. Government Printing Office, 1965.

Thorne, Wynne, ed., *Land and Water Use,* American Association for the Advancement of Science, 1963: Bailey Bros.

Wolman, Abel, "The Metabolism of Cities," *Scientific American,* September 1965.

*Also available in paperback edition.

†Only available in paperback edition.

ACKNOWLEDGEMENTS

The editors of this book are especially indebted to Charles Robinove, Hydrologist with the U.S. Geological Survey in Washington, D.C., and the following other members of its staff: in Washington—Raymond L. Nace, Research Hydrologist; Walter B. Langbein, Research Hydrologist; Herbert A. Swenson, Research Chemist; Walton H. Durum, Research Chemist; H. G. Thomasson, Engineer; Mae E. Thiesen; George C. Taylor Jr., Hydrologist; Frank Forrester, Chief Information Officer; Elwood Bear, Assistant Information Officer; in Denver—Gerald M. Richmond, Research Geologist; in Menlo Park, California—Ivan K. Barnes, Research Geophysicist, and David M. Hopkins, Geologist; in Phoenix—Mary Louise Brown; James M. Cahill, Engineer Technician; Eugene P. Patten Jr., Geologist in Charge, Analogue Model Unit; Geraldine M. Robinson, Hydraulic Engineer, and H. E. Skibitzke, Mathematician in Charge; also, at the Geological Survey of Canada, to V. K. Prest, Senior Geologist, and Douglas R. Grant, Pleistocene Section, Economic Geology Division. In addition, the editors wish to thank the following persons and institutions: Robert Adams, Director, and other members of the staff of the Oriental Institute, University of Chicago; Norman Bray, Instructor in Chemistry, Hunter College of the City University of New York; Wallace S. Broecker, Professor of Geochemistry, Rhodes W. Fairbridge, Professor of Geology, and L. Carrington Goodrich, Professor Emeritus of Chinese, Columbia University; C. W. Brownell, General Superintendent, and G. T. Kalman, Production Manager, of the DeLaval Separator Co., Poughkeepsie, New York; Mrs. James Burke; Frank Busby, Oceanologist, U.S. Naval Oceanographic Office, Washington, D.C.; John Cairns Jr., Curator and Assistant Chairman, Limnology Department, Academy of Natural Sciences, Philadelphia; Alfred R. Golzé, Chief Engineer, California Water Resources Agency, Sacramento; Tony Gow, Glaciologist, Cold Regions Research and Engineering Laboratory, Hanover, New Hampshire; Sheldon Judson, Professor of Geology, Princeton University; Richard M. Klein, Curator of Plant Physiology, New York Botanical Gardens; Helmut Landsberg, Chief Climatologist, U.S. Weather Bureau, Washington, D.C.; Garrick M. Lightowler, Information Officer, The World Bank, Washington, D.C.; J. W. O'Meara, Information Officer, Office of Saline Water, Washington, D.C.; Ben Osborn, Conservationist, *Soil Conservation Magazine,* U.S. Department of Agriculture, Washington, D.C.; The Peace Corps, Washington, D.C.; Knut Schmidt-Nielsen, Professor of Physiology, Department of Zoology, Duke University; Alan Schulman, Associate Professor of Ancient History, Queens College; James Shepherd, TIME-LIFE News Service, New Delhi, India; Sardar Nirmal J. Singh, Consul for Press and Cultural Affairs, Consulate General of India, New York City; William G. Van Dorn, Senior Engineer, Scripps Institute of Oceanography, University of California, La Jolla; H. T. U. Smith, Chairman, Department of Geology, University of Massachusetts; and Scott Warthin, Professor of Geology, Vassar College.

INDEX

Numerals in italics indicate a photograph or painting of the subject mentioned.

A

B

C

D

E

F

G

PICTURE CREDITS

Credits for pictures from left to right are separated by commas, top to bottom by dashes.

CHAPTER 1: 8—Marta Huth. 10—Drawings by Joseph Del Gaudio. 14—Drawing by Joseph Del Gaudio. 17 to 31—Photos by Ken Kay, drawings by George V. Kelvin.

CHAPTER 2: 32—NASA. 35—Drawing by John Condon. 38—Courtesy Dr. Raymond L. Nace. 41—Drawing by John Condon. 43—David Moore from Black Star. 44, 45—William Vandivert. 46, 47—Otto Hagel—Ansel Adams from Magnum. 48—John Dominis. 49—Brian Brake from Magnum. 50, 51—Drawings by Matt Greene. 52, 43—Fritz Goro.

CHAPTER 3: 54—Emil Schulthess, Conzett & Huber, from Black Star. 56, 57—Drawings by John Condon. 59—Drawings by Joseph Del Gaudio. 61—Drawings by Nicholas Fasciano. 63—A. Y. Owen. 64, 65—Drawings by Joseph Lombardero. 66—U.S. Geological Survey, Water Resources Division—Joe Munroe. 67, 68, 69—Ken Kay. 70—Joe Munroe—drawings by Lowell Hess. 71—Drawing by Lowell Hess, Ken Kay. 72—Ken Kay—U.S. Geological Survey, Water Resources Division. 73—Ken Kay.

CHAPTER 4: 74—James Burke. 76—Drawing by Donald and Ann Crews. 77, 78, 79—Drawings by Nicholas Fasciano. 81, 83—Drawings by Nicholas Fasciano courtesy Dr. Luna B. Leopold. 85—Ken Kay. 86, 87—Drawing by Ken Fagg. 88, 89—Drawings by Donald and Ann Crews, Dr. Austin Post. 90—Official U.S. Navy Photograph. 91—Steven C. Wilson from Meridian (4)—Alicia Hills Moore, A. Y. Owen. 92, 93—Drawing by Donald and Ann Crews, Steven C. Wilson from Meridian—N. R. Farbman. 94, 95—Drawing by Donald and Ann Crews, Frank Scherschel, John P. Porter. 96, 97—William A. Garnett, U.S. Geological Survey, Water Resources Division, drawings by Donald and Ann Crews. 98, 99—Drawings by Donald and Ann Crews, Steven C. Wilson from Meridian, John Dominis. 100, 101—Drawing by Ken Fagg.

CHAPTER 5: 102—Steven C. Wilson from Meridian. 105—Drawing by Nicholas Fasciano. 106—Figure by Leslie Martin, chart by James Alexander. 111—Ansel Adams from Magnum. 112 to 119—Drawings by Leslie Martin.

CHAPTER 6: 120—Pierre Streit from Black Star. 123—Drawing by Nicholas Fasciano. 124—Culver Pictures, Inc. 125—Drawing by James Alexander. 127—Drawings by James Alexander. 129—Vidyavrata from Frances L. Orkin. 130, 131—Photos by James Burke, drawings by Otto van Eersel. 132—Marilyn Silverstone from Magnum. 133—James Burke—Leonard Wolfe. 134, 135—James Burke. 136, 137—Leonard Wolfe, Maitland A. Edey. 138—Raghubir Singh from Nancy Palmer Photo Agency. 139—Howard Sochurek. 140, 141—E. Newby—Sunil Janah, Raghubir Singh from Nancy Palmer Photo Agency. 142, 143—E. Boubat-*Réalités*.

CHAPTER 7: 144—Margaret Bourke-White. 146—The Bettmann Archive. 148—Drawing by Donald and Ann Crews. 151—Drawing by Donald and Ann Crews. 152—Drawing by George V. Kelvin. 155—Howard Sochurek. 156, 157—Andreas Feininger. 158, 159—Estafoto, Dmitri Kessel. 160, 161—Foto KLM Aerocarto N.V., except centre: Aero-Camera, Luchthaven-Rotterdam. 162, 163—Albert Fenn, John Dominis. 164, 165—J. R. Eyerman—Ralph Crane, Howard Sochurek. 166, 167—Left: Charles Krutch—Ted Russell; right: Gordon Coster. 168, 169—Ben Martin.

CHAPTER 8: 170—Otto Hagel. 173—James Alexander. 174, 175—Drawings by George V. Kelvin. 177—Drawing by Nicholas Fasciano. 179—Frank Scherschel. 180, 181—Chicago Bridge and Iron Company, City of Portland Water Bureau, Denver Board of Water Commissioners. 182, 183—Drawings by Otto van Eersel. 184, 185—Gordon Tenney. 186, 187—Ray Manley Photograph courtesy Stearns-Roger Corporation, drawing by Nicholas Fasciano. 188, 189—Drawings by Nicholas Fasciano. 190, 191—U.S. Geological Survey, Water Resources Division. 193—Graph by James Alexander.

XXX

Typesetting by C. E. Dawkins (Typesetters) Ltd., London, S.E.1
Smeets Lithographers, Weert, Printed in Holland
Bound by Proost en Brandt N.V., Amsterdam